HABITS of the HEART

RICHARD M. SIDDOWAY

BOOKCRAFT

SALT LAKE CITY, UTAH

Library of Congress Catalog Card Number: 95-83315
ISBN 1-57008-225-1

First Printing, 1996

Printed in the United States of America

PREFACE

♥

*O*ver three decades ago, while attending the University of Utah, I had the pleasure of taking a class from Dr. Lowell Bennion at the LDS institute of religion. Although I find it difficult to remember many of the classes or lectures from my college days, I distinctly remember a lesson Dr. Bennion gave about the different kinds of love. He discussed how poorly we deal with the concept of love in the English language. His lesson led us through different levels of love. He began with the rather selfish concept of romantic love, which tends to create within the love-smitten the desire to possess the other person. He led us through the concept of love expressed in service to others, and concluded with the love epitomized by the Savior's selfless sacrifice. Eros, agape, phileo.

Dr. Bennion's words have come back to haunt me over the years. I often have found myself wondering, in quiet contemplation, how mature my ability to love has grown. Perhaps it is easier to see in others than in oneself the deeper meanings of the expressions of love.

All of the stories in this book are based upon actual incidents. Because of the nature of the situations, however, the names, locations, and events have been altered to preserve the anonymity of those involved. In some cases individuals or events have been combined. The intent is not to deceive but to entertain.

I am indebted to those involved for their abilities to display love in a multitude of ways. I must give credit to my wife for her unstinting support and to those at Bookcraft who have expressed their faith in me, especially Cory Maxwell. I am also indebted to Alexis de Tocqueville, who coined the phrase "a habit of the heart."

CHAPTER 1

♥

First love is often bittersweet.
It is filled with fantasy and
daydreams that never seem
to be fulfilled.

$\mathcal{I}$t was her hair I first noticed. Her hair was cut in a pageboy style, turned under at the ends, shoulder length, and the color of honey. We had a jar of Miller's honey on the shelf in our kitchen at home. I often turned it over and placed it upside down on our kitchen table. An air bubble moved slowly upward through the amber nectar like a large transparent marble. Margo's hair was the same color as that honey. I watched that hair from my vantage point two rows behind her. We were in the third grade. I was eight years old.

Our school building was a two-story brick structure on the corner of McClelland Street and Harrison Avenue. Across McClelland to the west was a fenced playground where we spent recesses and learned to play baseball and kickball. During the winter months, when the playground was covered with snow, we played "fox and geese." At other times we fell backward in the snow and moved our arms up and down to make snow angels.

It was during one such recess, late in the school year, that I sat against the fence and watched Margo. My next-door neighbor, Alan, squatted down next to me. "What's ya doin'?" he asked.

"Nothin'."

"How come you ain't playing baseball with the other guys?" In all fairness, only about half of the kids on the playground were involved in any kind of play, organized or not. The rest of us just stood or sat near the fence and watched. Those of us who sat watching were typically the less skilled at whatever game was going on at the time. Since I was the youngest and smallest member of my class, I often chose to sit out the activities at recess time.

"You look kinda sad," pursued Alan. "Somethin' wrong?"

I sighed. Margo was leaning against the fence behind home plate, her fingers clutching the chain-link fence. Her honey hair glowed in the April sunshine. No one could possibly have been more beautiful. I quickly looked away. There was no way I could let Alan know the desires of my heart. He couldn't keep a secret for all the tea in China. I shook my head. "Nothing's wrong," I said quietly.

Delmar Porter was up at bat. I focused my attention on him. Delmar was the biggest boy in our class. I suppose it's normal for the big to pick on the small, but Delmar carried it to the extreme. I was often the target of his abuse.

The ball was pitched and Delmar's bat connected. The ball went flying deep into left field. Delmar charged furiously down the baseline toward first base. The left fielder was running toward the ball. The first baseman stood, hands on hips, watching the ball bounce in the outfield. Delmar rounded first and started toward second base. The fielder reached the ball and threw it with all his might in the general direction of third base. Delmar rounded second and thundered toward third. Just as Delmar reached third base, the ball bounced to a halt about ten feet short of the third baseman. Delmar glanced over his shoulder as the third baseman ran to retrieve the ball, and then picked up steam as he raced toward home. The third baseman flung the ball toward home. The catcher fumbled the ball for a moment and then gained control. He stuck the ball in his gloved left hand toward the charging Delmar. Delmar crashed full force into the catcher. The ball squirted loose. The catcher landed flat on his back and let out a scream of pain. Delmar lost his balance and tumbled into the backstop just in front of Margo.

"Oh!" exclaimed Margo. She quickly ran around the fence to where Delmar now stood, dusting off his corduroy pants. "Are you hurt?"

Delmar shook his head.

Miss Nacarato, our playground supervisor, was kneeling beside the catcher, who was struggling to catch his breath. "Delmar," she snarled, "that was totally unnecessary."

"He got in my way," shrugged Delmar. Just then the bell rang, calling us back to class.

"Boy," said Alan as we walked across McClelland Street to the school. "I hope I never get in Delmar's way."

"Me neither," I exclaimed quietly as we entered our ancient building.

I took my seat two desks behind Margo as our teacher began giving us the spelling words for the week. I gazed at Margo's golden locks and began to fantasize. I could see myself standing at bat with Delmar pitching. He threw the ball as hard as he could, but I hit it easily. The ball flew over the heads of the fielders, and I began running around the bases. Before the fielder had even reached the ball, I was crossing home base, and Margo was running out from behind the fence to hug and congratulate me. "Enough," said our teacher, Miss Heacock.

"What?" I said.

"Enough. Spell enough," she repeated.

"Oh, e-n-o-u-g-h," I spelled. My reverie was finished for the day. Arithmetic followed spelling, and then we worked on science until lunch.

There was no school lunch provided at our school. Most of us brought our lunches in brown paper bags that had our names written on them. For my birthday late in March, my Aunt Ruth had given me a Superman lunch box complete with a thermos jug that fit inside it. The outside of the lunch box was emblazoned with a picture of the Man of Steel flying above Metropolis. The blue thermos jug was especially impressive, with the red and yellow *S* from Superman's chest printed on the side. Although we all brought our lunches, we were able to purchase a small bottle of milk or orange drink for two cents. The milk and orange drink were kept as cold as possible in the school, but were still often lukewarm when we drank them. My thermos jug was able to keep my milk cold. On rare occasions my mother filled my thermos with Kool-Aid. Small as these pleasures were, they seemed significant at the time. My Superman lunch box gave me considerable pride.

When we were dismissed for lunch, I walked to the small coatroom in the back of the classroom where our lunches were kept. I quickly scanned the shelves looking for Superman, but he was nowhere to be seen. Frantically I searched behind the remaining brown bags, but my lunch box was gone. I ran to Miss Heacock's desk. "Somebody stole my lunch box!" I screamed.

"Settle down," said my teacher. "Let's just go look for it again." She accompanied me to the coatroom. All of the brown paper bags had now been claimed, and my lunch box was nowhere in sight. "Are you sure you brought your lunch today?" she quizzed.

"Yes, yes, I'm sure," I replied, hopping on one leg and then the other.

"Did you have your name on your lunch bag?"

"It wasn't a lunch bag, it was a lunch box, a Superman lunch box. My aunt gave it to me for a birthday present. I've only had it for two weeks, and somebody took it." My voice grew shriller and shriller as I continued rambling on.

Miss Heacock searched the shelves a final time and then said, "Let's go down to the office." She took me by the hand and led me there. I could see it now. The police were about to be informed and a full-scale investigation would begin. Each of my classmates would be questioned, and at last the culprit would confess. I would get my lunch box back, and the thief would be hauled away to jail.

We reached the office, and my teacher said, "Do you know your phone number?" I blurted it out. Miss Heacock picked up the phone and dialed my home. "Hello," she said, "this is Miss Heacock. I think we have a little problem here at school." My mother said something in reply.

"No, no, he's not in trouble, but apparently something has happened to his lunch box. He didn't by chance leave it home this morning, did he?" Again there was a pause. "Well, we'll just have to see where it ended up, I suppose," said Miss Heacock, pausing. "That seems like a good idea. I'll have him meet you halfway. Thank you." She hung up the phone.

"Your mother says you left with your lunch box this morning. Is it possible you put it down somewhere?" I shook my head. "Well, anyway, your mother is going to make you a sandwich. She'd like you to start walking toward your home and she'll start walking toward school. After lunch we'll see if anyone knows where your lunch box is."

I started walking the four blocks toward home. My mother met me and gave me a sandwich and two pennies. I ate the sandwich as I walked back to school. I

5

bought a bottle of orange drink with the two pennies. I looked around the school yard. There was no Superman lunch box in sight.

"Class," said our teacher later, when all of us were in our seats again, "did any of you see a lunch box on the shelves in the coatroom? One seems to have come up missing." I looked around the room. A few shoulders shrugged; quite a few heads shook back and forth slightly. "If any of you see a Superman lunch box, please return it to me and I'll get it back to the owner."

I couldn't believe Miss Heacock was treating this so lightly. My Superman lunch box had been stolen, and she was behaving as if I had just misplaced it. To be fair, I had reported a box of crayons, a pair of gloves, and two stocking caps stolen on several earlier occasions during the year. But this was different. Even though all of those other items had been found where I had laid them down for a minute, I knew I had put my lunch box on the shelf and someone had stolen it.

Throughout the rest of the school day my mind was not on my work. I was in a turmoil. Then a plan formed in my head. Whoever stole my lunch box would have to take it home. I'd just make sure I was the first one out of the building, and I'd take my position on the corner of the school yard, where I could see everyone who left. The lunch box was big enough that it would be hard to conceal. Even if Miss Heacock believed I had set it down somewhere, I knew I could identify the thief.

At last, the final bell of the day rang and I raced out of the room to put my plan into action. There was a drinking fountain in front of the school. It looked like a bronze morning glory and had three fountain heads from which we could drink. By standing just to the west of the fountain I could see all of the students who exited the school. I took my position there and tried to look as casual as possible. The other kids poured out of the building on my heels. I looked at every student I could as the school grounds emptied. Apparently Superman had turned into Clark Kent. I waited until everyone had left, but my lunch box did not appear.

Dejectedly I walked home. At least there I would have someone to give me solace. My mother was waiting as I walked through the door. "You're late," she said. "Did you find where you'd left your lunch box?"

"I left it on the shelf where it's supposed to be," I snarled. "Somebody stole it."

"Don't be rude, young man," she said. "Now, go change your clothes and you can help me get dinner ready."

My father was even less understanding. At dinner he said, "I don't know why your Aunt Ruth even thought about giving you a lunch box. You're always losing things."

The next morning I took my lunch in a paper bag. Superman did not appear that day, nor any day for the next two weeks.

❤

Liberty Park was located about four blocks from our school. An annual field day was held there near the end of the school year. On Friday Miss Heacock announced that the following Tuesday we would be walking to Liberty Park for field day. She gave each of us an information sheet to take home to our parents. We were to bring a sack lunch. The school was going to provide milk or orange drink, and we would be walking from school to the park for our activities and then we'd walk back to school at the end of the day. There was a place on the information sheet for our parents to give their permission by signing their names.

On Monday Miss Heacock asked for all of the permission slips. She apparently was worried about someone getting lost on this four-block expedition. On the chalk-board she drew a map to show us how to get from the school to the park. Fate had given Miss Heacock a class with equal numbers of boys and girls. One girl had moved out during Christmas vacation, but another girl had moved in, so the balance had been maintained. "Class," she said, "I think it's important to learn proper manners, so tomorrow before our walk to and from the park, I'm going to pair each girl with a boy. Girls, on the way to the park, you make sure you walk on the inside of the sidewalk. Boys, you make sure you walk on the outside. The reason for this social custom is no longer important, but I think you need to know your manners."

A plan sprang into my mind. Somehow I needed to make sure that I was paired with Margo. The two of us would have an uninterrupted stroll together to and from Liberty Park.

"There's another reason I want you to be in pairs," continued Miss Heacock. "That way you'll be able to keep track of each other. It's called the buddy system. That means, boys, you should know where your partner is throughout field day. Do you understand?" All of our heads nodded.

Throughout the rest of the day I schemed and planned how to make sure I was paired with Margo. I tried to figure out how Miss Heacock would select the pairs. I counted the number of boys in each row. I counted the number of girls. If Miss Heacock began on the other side of the room and worked our way, I figured that I would be paired with Sandra, who sat between Margo and me. If, however, she started on our side of the room, Margo and I would end up walking together. I couldn't think of a way to politely suggest to Miss Heacock that she start on our side of the room. I left for home with no clear-cut plan.

The next morning Miss Heacock greeted us at the

door. "Just keep your lunches with you," she said. "We'll be leaving as soon as everyone gets here."

I clutched my brown bag tightly. "Please start on our side of the room," I whispered under my breath. When the last child was in place, Miss Heacock began calling out names at random. "Ann, you and Arthur stand up here by the door and get ready to start us on our trek. Barbara and Gregory, you're next."

My mind whirled. There was no apparent order to how the pairs were being formed. What was she doing? How could I make sure that Margo and I walked together?

"Lily and Delmar take your place. Thank you. Now, Margo . . ." *Oh, please, please,* I pleaded silently. "Margo and Dick, you're next." My heart did flip-flops within my chest. I picked up my lunch bag and tried to appear nonchalant as I walked to my place in line. Margo took her place beside me. I smiled at her. She smiled back. I'm sure the rest of the names were called out and the rest of the students took their places in line, but I remember none of that in the pure ecstasy of the moment.

"Arthur, Ann," said Miss Heacock, "take each other's hand and let's walk safely down to Liberty Park." Margo reached over and took my hand. My knees became so weak that I could barely walk. This was beyond my wildest expectations. We walked out the door of the school and down McClelland Street to Thirteenth South. Delmar and Lily walked ahead of Margo and me. They chatted and giggled as they walked along. I couldn't think of a single thing to say to Margo.

"Who do you want for fourth grade next year?" she asked me.

"I dunno," I mumbled back. "Who do you want?"

"Mr. Burningham. I've never had a man teacher, and I think it would be neat."

I looked at Margo's golden hair gleaming in the

spring sunshine. "I have a jar of honey at home," I blurted out.

Margo looked at me quizzically. "Oh?"

"Sometimes I turn it over and watch a bubble rise up through the honey."

"That's interesting," she said. Her forehead crinkled. "What else do you do for fun?"

"Oh, I just turn the jar back over and watch the bubble go the other way. It reminds me of you."

Margo's eyes widened. "A bubble reminds you of me?"

"Not the bubble; the honey—well, not really the honey; the color of the honey, I mean—well, it's kind of complicated."

"I see," said Margo. We lapsed back into silence until we neared our destination. "Are you going to run in the three-legged race?" she asked.

"I don't know, I haven't thought much about it," I stammered. "Are you going to?"

"If I can get someone to be my partner," said Margo. "It takes two, you know."

Delmar jerked his head around. "I'll be your partner if you want."

"Thank you, Delmar," she said.

We walked on in silence to Liberty Park. The relay races began shortly after we arrived. Delmar and Margo won the three-legged race. Lily, Delmar's partner, sat next to me on the grass. "You keeping an eye on Margo?"

"Trying to," I replied.

"Don't think Delmar even knows where I am," she complained.

When the relays were over, a school district truck pulled across the grass to where we'd been racing. In the back of the truck were bottles of milk and orange drink. Mr. Isaacson, the principal, climbed into the back of the truck and motioned for all of us to assemble. "It's time for lunch," he shouted. "Please sit together by your teacher so we can make sure we know where everyone is."

Lily and I walked over to the truck and picked out bottles of lukewarm orange drink. We walked back to where Miss Heacock was sitting in the shade of a tree. I spotted Margo and Delmar sitting on the other side of Miss Heacock's tree. Lily and I sat where we could see them. Margo spread a napkin on the grass and removed a sandwich from her lunch sack. Delmar reached into his enormous lunch sack and retrieved a thermos jug with a Superman logo. He looked straight at me and sneered. Tears of rage filled my eyes. I felt violated and powerless. "Miss Heacock," I cried out.

"Yes, what do you want?"

I looked at Delmar and imagined what he would do to me if I squealed on him. "Nothing," I said quietly.

The afternoon events were finished and we prepared to walk back to school. Margo approached me and said, "Will you walk back with Lily? I'm going to walk with Delmar."

"Why are you going to walk with him?" I tried to keep the venom from my voice.

" 'Cause he's going to let me have a drink from his thermos."

Lily and I walked behind Delmar and Margo. Her hair was not nearly as radiant as I remembered it.

CHAPTER 2

♥

*Love is best expressed when we
serve without thought
of repayment.*

Clyde Hooper was an ugly man. I suppose there
are kinder euphemisms, but bluntly put, he was an ugly
man. He was well over six feet tall and so thin that if he
turned sideways he'd hardly cast a shadow, except for
his Adam's apple, which jutted forward from his throat,
and his buck teeth, which jutted out nearly as far. His left
arm was frozen in a continual bend at the elbow, and his
hand bent down at the wrist, with immobile, clawlike fingers. A scar ran from just below his right ear past the corner of his eye and disappeared beneath the straw hat he
always wore. His red-rimmed right eyelid drooped behind his eyeglasses. The lenses were so thick and heavy
that his glasses perpetually slid down his nose. Clyde
would absent-mindedly push his spectacles back in place
every few seconds. Clyde Hooper was an ugly man.

As we walked home from school each afternoon, we
took a shortcut up an alley that ran behind the houses
facing Harrison Avenue to the north and Browning
Avenue to the south. In a small white house that faced
Browning Avenue lived Mrs. Proust, a widow of many
years who had lost her husband in World War I. Except

for a menagerie of cats, dogs, rabbits, and canaries, she lived alone. In her backyard was a smaller two-room guest house. It was in this small wooden structure that Clyde Hooper lived. It was only about twelve feet square, with a steep, sloping roof shingled in silvery gray cedar shakes. The walls of this building were covered with horizontal eight-inch boards painted white. There was a small covered front porch, perhaps four feet square on the side, facing Mrs. Proust's driveway. The back of Clyde Hooper's house was about three feet from the alleyway. A broken-down board fence with a gate ran along the back property line.

Frequently as we walked home from school, we'd see Clyde outside his little house. Those of us who were younger were frightened by this gangling, misshapen man, and accelerated our pace up the alley. Those who were older, the sixth-grade students, thought they were braver and called out insults to Clyde Hooper. Clyde appeared not to notice our run past his house, nor the remarks cast in his direction.

In the autumn of 1948 I entered the fourth grade, and my cousin Bill, who was living with us at the time, entered the sixth. We were walking home from school together one day and saw Clyde in Mrs. Proust's backyard. I began to speed up my pace, but Bill grabbed my arm. In some unspoken rite of passage, Bill stopped and called out, "Hey, four-eyes, why don't you do us all a favor and move?" Bill chuckled at his display of wit and continued up the alley. Clyde seemed not to notice.

"How come you did that, Bill?" I asked.

Bill gave a two-part answer that seemed adequate at the time. "'Cause he's different, and besides, everybody does it." Only in my later years did I realize how many battles have been fought for those same two totally ridiculous reasons.

That night Clyde Hooper's name came up at the dinner table. "I believe tomorrow is Brother Hooper's birthday," my mother said. "He's such a pitiful sight. I think Sister Proust is an angel for letting him live in that guest house of hers."

"Umm," my father replied, not really interested in the conversation.

"I thought maybe I'd bake him a birthday cake in the morning," continued my mother. "The boys could take it to him after school tomorrow."

Bill glanced at me. He had a way of looking out of the corner of his eye and then looking quickly away when he was nervous. "I've got to stay after school for a few minutes tomorrow," he said. "I don't think I'll be able to help take the cake to Mr. Hooper." Maybe Clyde Hooper had heard Bill's taunt today, maybe not; but there was no sense taking a chance.

I knew at that moment I'd be going to Clyde Hooper's alone. Bill's fertile brain seemed to be able to produce excuses at the drop of a hat. Mine was not nearly as quick . . . or as devious. I also knew that I was scared.

"You ever look at those shoes he wears?" my father interjected. "Must be number twelves. Real clodhoppers."

Bill's brain whirled into gear. "Clodhoppers for Clyde Hooper. Maybe they should have called him Clod Hopper." Bill began to chortle.

"Bill," my mother said sharply, "there is no need to pick on that unfortunate man. I'll have no more of that!" But I knew that from then on he'd be called Clod Hopper by my cousin Bill.

The following day Bill hung around with some of the sixth-graders after school while I walked home with my fourth-grade friends. We ran full bore past Clyde Hooper's house. "My mom baked him a birthday cake," I wheezed breathlessly, pointing over my shoulder with my thumb. "I've gotta take it to him when I get home. Anybody want to come with me?" I asked hopefully. There was a professed new interest in cleaning bedrooms that kept my friends from accompanying me.

My mother, true to her word, had baked a birthday cake. "I hope he likes checkerboard cakes," she said. "It's a pink and white one. I didn't know how many candles to put on it, so I just wrote 'Happy Birthday, Clyde.'" The cake was on a cookie sheet. "Now, just be careful taking this cake to Brother Hooper, and make sure you bring the cookie sheet back."

This meant I could not just leave the cake on the doorstep. I actually would have to talk with Clyde Hooper. "Do I hafta?" I asked plaintively.

My mother ignored my whine. "Hurry," she said, "but be careful." And I was pushed out our front door carrying the birthday cake. I walked carefully the half block west to the corner and then turned and walked straight north toward the Widow Proust's. The autumn leaves were falling, and my feet swished through golden aspen and red-orange maple leaves as I trudged slowly down the road. There was a faint odor of burning leaves that mingled with the smell of birthday cake.

Mrs. Proust was outside raking her front yard. A half-dozen cats chased each other around her feet and pounced upon the leaves that were shifting in the slight breeze. *Perhaps,* I thought, *I can leave the cake with her, or at least get her to take it to Clyde.*

"Hello," Mrs. Proust called out as I approached her neatly fenced front yard. "What do you have there?" She pushed up the floppy brim of her gardening hat. "Oh, the cake for Mr. Hooper. Your mother phoned me earlier this afternoon and mentioned you'd be bringing it by. I do think it's so nice of your mother to remember him on this special day. Just go right around back. I'm sure he's home." She gestured toward the driveway.

"Thank you," I said as politely as my apprehension permitted. I walked slowly down the driveway, fear mounting with each step. As I rounded the back corner of the house I saw Clyde Hooper standing to the side of his little home, brushing something with his right hand from the front of the denim apron he always wore. A lump rushed into my throat so that I felt my Adam's apple must look as big as his. "Mr. Hooper," I croaked. He turned slowly in my direction. He pushed the glasses up his nose. "Happy birthday." It was all I could think to say as I proffered the cake.

He walked toward me with his scarecrow gait and looked at the birthday offering. His glasses slid down his ample nose. He pushed them back into place. "For me?" He looked into my face. I nodded my head. "But who? Why?"

"Isn't it your birthday?" I squeaked.

A little smile seemed to be trying to attach itself to Clyde Hooper's face. "Well, yes, but you know, I'd almost forgotten." His glasses slid down his nose. I noticed tears in his eyes as he pushed them back into place. "Thank you, my boy. Thank you."

"My mom wonders if you can put the cake onto a plate or something so I can take the cookie sheet home," I said as I furtively handed him the cake.

His brow furrowed. "Of course, of course, just a minute." He took the cookie sheet in his good right hand and walked slowly to his front door. I wondered if he could open the door with his gnarled left hand, but the door was ajar, and he pushed it open with his shoulder. A moment later he reappeared with the cookie sheet. "I'd ask you in, my boy, but there's so little room. Thank you again, and thank your good mother for me."

I turned to go, cookie sheet in hand, when I heard a chant begin on the other side of the back fence. "Clyde Hooper's a clodhopper. Clyde Hooper's a clodhopper."

He straightened up slowly, then his chin dropped down on his chest and he walked, storklike, back to his house. Suddenly an apple core flew over the fence and bounced off Clyde's roof. I turned and walked down the driveway.

"You're a good boy," said Mrs. Proust as I came into sight. "Tell your mother thank you from me as well." I nodded my head and began the journey home with the cookie sheet. Bill arrived a few moments after I did.

"Did you deliver the cake to old Clod Hopper?" he asked. I nodded. "And he didn't hurt you or nothin'?" I shook my head.

"Mrs. Proust and Mr. Hooper thanked you for the cake," I said to my mother as I opened the back door into our kitchen. She smiled. The kitchen smelled wonderful. Not only had my mother baked a birthday cake for Clyde, she'd also baked one for our family, as well as several loaves of bread. She handed me a thick slice of warm bread covered with butter.

"Thank you for taking the cake to Brother Hooper," she replied. "I just hope it brings a little happiness into his life. He seems so . . ." She struggled for the right word. "So . . . alone."

♥

The next day was Saturday. Bill and I were playing in the backyard of our next-door neighbor, Alan, when the two Simpson brothers, Jim and Ralph, appeared down the gravel driveway. "Hey, Alan," said Jim, the older of the two. "Can we have some of the horse chestnuts from your front yard?"

Alan had three horse chestnut trees in front of his house. During late September and early October they rained down a cascade of chestnuts upon the sidewalk and front yard. Alan's mother often asked us to clean up the chestnuts and their spiky husks. It was not a job we enjoyed, although we always kept a few chestnuts to polish and turn into rings by boring holes through them. "Sure," said Alan, "you can have all you want. Just make sure you take the husks, too."

Jim Simpson was a ninth-grader; his brother, Ralph, was a year younger. They were nearly carbon copies of each other, with unruly thatches of reddish-blond hair and out-thrust chins. Bill found them to be kindred, if somewhat older, spirits. They always seemed to be up to some scheme. "What's you gonna do with those chestnuts?" asked Bill. Jim crooked his finger in Bill's direction and motioned him to his side. Whispers were exchanged, punctuated with giggles. The Simpsons gathered up sufficient horse chestnuts to fill the small basket they'd brought with them. Bill helped. More whispers and giggles were exchanged as the Simpson brothers headed down the hill toward home.

Monday afternoon, Bill and I started home from school. The sky was overcast and a brisk wind was blowing. As we approached Clyde's house, Bill paused. "You go on home," he said. "I'll be there in a few minutes."

"What's up?" I asked.

"Just waiting for the Simpsons," replied Bill. "I'll be home soon." His look told me not to ask any further questions. I shrugged my shoulders and caught up with the rest of my fourth-grade friends.

Just as we were sitting down for dinner, the telephone rang. My mother, who has never let a phone ring more than twice before answering it, jumped to her feet. "Hurry," grumbled my father, "we don't want everything to get cold." My mother returned in just a moment, her forehead furrowed and her lips pouted. "What's the matter?" asked my father.

"That was Sister Proust. Someone pelted Clyde Hooper's little house with chestnuts this afternoon. She just wanted to know if I'd heard anything about it." She looked at me as her eyebrows lowered. "Do either of you boys know anything about it?"

I shook my head slowly.

"Bill?" asked my mother.

Bill's eyes shifted toward me questioningly; then, relieved, he looked at my mother and quickly shook his head.

"Sister Proust said she thought they were bigger boys, but I just wanted to make sure. That poor man doesn't need any more grief in his life." She sighed. Dinner began.

After dinner Bill and I retired to the bedroom we shared. "I didn't throw any of the chestnuts," he said defensively. "The Simpsons threw them all. I was just there to watch. Man, that first handful they threw, old Clod came flying out of his house like he was being shot at. No harm done, though. He's just got a few chestnuts to pick up, that's all."

"I don't want to hear about it, Bill. Just leave him alone."

"Getting soft on me? We ain't hurting anybody or anything, we're just making old Clod jump. And don't go telling your mom neither, if you know what's good for you." Bill stalked out of the bedroom.

In the next week more chestnuts and some overripe apples and pears ended up on Clyde Hooper's roof. Increasingly Bill did not walk home from school with me. His attachment to the Simpson brothers generated mixed emotions. I was, of course, a little jealous, but also relieved that he had not coerced me into his attacks on Clyde Hooper's house.

Halloween approached. Decorations sprang up around our neighborhood. A couple of blocks from our house was a farmers market that sold produce. Pumpkins arrived and Bill and I were each allowed to select one to carve into a jack-o-lantern. Cornstalks were bundled and placed on our front porch. Our carved pumpkins would have candles placed in them to give light for the trick-or-treaters.

My schoolroom was decorated with cut-out pumpkins, black cats, and witches. My teacher announced the annual Halloween parade through all of the classrooms and encouraged us to wear costumes to school. The parade each year was made bearable by the teachers giving each of us a treat as we marched out the door of their rooms. At dinner I discussed plans for a costume with my parents. Bill had already decided to wear his Dracula cape from the past year. For the past three years I had been a clown. I wanted a costume that was more dignified.

"How about being a clown?" my father suggested.

"Can't I be something different this year?" I pleaded.

"Well," said my mother, "we already have a clown outfit, and you look so cute in it." Just what I wanted to hear—I looked *cute*. "But maybe it's getting too small."

"It's too small," I quickly agreed. "I could go as a bat, or a hunchback, or . . ."

Bill interrupted, "Or a Clod Hopper."

My mother's countenance darkened. "We'll think of something." In the end I went as a clown. I hadn't grown quite enough to make it too small.

Dracula and his clown sidekick walked home from school after the Halloween parade. For some reason we decided against walking up the alley and chose to walk up Browning Avenue instead. Mrs. Proust was on her porch trying to make spiderwebs out of yarn. I glanced down the driveway. Clyde Hooper had created a scarecrow on his little porch. The body was made of stuffed clothing, and the head was made of an enormous pumpkin.

"Does anyone ever trick-or-treat Clyde's place?" I asked Bill.

He glanced down the driveway and saw the scarecrow. "I don't think so. It's sort of spooky when it's dark. I mean, who'd want to go clear to the backyard?"

"Maybe I will this year," I mused. "Somebody ought to visit him, I guess." We hurried on home to prepare for the evening's events.

❤

Halloween is a holiday of joy for small children, a holiday in which the unbridled consumption of candy is permitted. It is a holiday of great concern for police officers, a holiday in which pranks are somehow tolerated; pranks which might otherwise lead to stern lectures or even detention.

Bill and I had been trick-or-treating for nearly two hours, had bags full of candy, and were headed home up Browning Avenue. Mrs. Proust added to our largess with a popcorn ball. "I'm going back to Clyde's place," I announced to Bill, who reluctantly agreed to accompany me. We left Mrs. Proust's front porch and turned down the long driveway to Clyde Hooper's. The candle in the scarecrow's pumpkin head gave flickering light to the porch.

Bill hesitated. "You go first," he said. He hung back in the shadows as I cautiously made my way to the porch.

I looked for a doorbell; there was none. I rapped timidly on the door with my knuckles. "Trick or treat," I croaked. The door swung open noisily on its hinges.

Clyde Hooper looked down at my clown face. His eyebrows knitted as he stared at me. "You're the only one, boy. You're the only trick-or-treater I've had in over ten years." He stepped back into his house, reappeared, and dropped something into my bag. The door swung noisily shut. I walked back into the total blackness of the driveway.

"What did he give you?" whispered Bill as I passed his hiding place.

"I don't know. He just dropped something into my bag. I couldn't see what it was. Why don't you go up and see. He won't hurt you."

Bill summoned his courage and inched his way up to the doorway. "Trick or treat."

Clyde Hooper's door creaked open. He gazed intently into Bill's face. "Another one," he mused. "For ten years no one, and now two brave trick-or-treaters." He retrieved something from the house and dropped it into Bill's bag. Bill scurried quickly from the porch and joined me in the driveway.

"What did you get?" I asked.

"I don't know. He just dropped it into my bag." We continued to trick-or-treat ourselves on home. It was after eight-thirty when we arrived. Our bedtime was nine o'clock.

"You boys took long enough," my father said as we sat down in the middle of the living room floor to sort our candy. I munched on a Snickers bar retrieved from the top of my sack. "You're usually home much earlier than tonight. I was beginning to worry. You know, after the treats have been given out, we sometimes have tricks." He was sitting in his favorite chair reading the newspaper.

Before we were able to dump our cache of candy onto the floor, we heard a siren in the distance. It quickly grew louder. When the red lights flashed through our front window and continued down the street, we all ran onto our front porch. The fire truck turned on the corner and headed toward Mrs. Proust's home. We hurried there as well, attracted like moths to a flame—and flames there were. Clyde Hooper's home was burning fiercely. By the time the firemen strung their hoses, it was clear there would be little to save, for the entire wooden structure was engulfed in flames. In fact, the majority of the firemen's efforts seemed to be concentrated on keeping Mrs.

Proust's home from suffering the same fate as Clyde Hooper's. Clyde and Mrs. Proust stood in Mrs. Proust's front yard. Tears streamed down both of their cheeks.

An hour later, the firemen left. We had been forced home by my father and told to get ready for bed. Sleep was long in coming. "I wonder how the fire got started," I said to no one in particular. Bill was silent. "We didn't even sort out our candy," I exclaimed, although I was already mildly sick from the amount of candy I'd consumed. The bag of goodies was on the floor at the foot of my bed. "I guess we'll do it tomorrow."

❤

The next afternoon as we were walking home from school, we saw that the alleyway was blocked off with a sawhorse. We were forced to walk up Browning Avenue. Clyde Hooper and Mrs. Proust were standing on Mrs. Proust's front porch. Bill immediately scurried across the street away from them, but something drew me there. "I'm really sorry," I said, not knowing what else to say.

Clyde Hooper looked down at me. "Ah, the boy with the birthday cake, my little clown friend. I'm sorry, too," he said softly.

"What will you do? Where will you go?" I asked him.

Tears coursed down Mrs. Proust's cheeks. "We don't know, we just don't know."

"Oh, I'll find someplace," said Clyde. He looked at Mrs. Proust. "I'm just sorry I won't be here to help you."

"Clyde lost everything in the fire," said Mrs. Proust. "All of his work, all of his beautiful carvings are gone. Gone up in smoke. Oh, those foolish, foolish boys."

"I don't understand," I said.

"I saw two boys dash out of the alleyway and push over Clyde's scarecrow. I don't know why the candle kept burning, but it did. The scarecrow was stuffed with newspaper. It caught on fire—almost exploded—and set the house on fire," said Mrs. Proust.

"Now, Milly," said Clyde, "I'm sure they weren't trying to do any damage. It was just a prank. It just had unfortunate results. But I'm so sorry your little guest house is gone. It was such a quiet place to work. I'll miss it." There was wistfulness and resignation in his voice.

"I'm really sorry," I said again, not quite understanding all of what I'd heard.

"Thank you," was all Clyde said.

In the uncomfortable silence I left the front porch and headed home. Bill was waiting at the bottom of our hill. I gave him my version of what had happened. He said nothing. We arrived home. My mother was just hanging up the telephone when we walked in.

"Did you boys hear how the Hooper fire started?" she challenged. She continued without waiting for our answer. "By some thoughtless boys who thought they were just having fun. They went on a rampage through this neighborhood. They destroyed decorations, they threw our cornstalks all over the front yard, they smashed pumpkins, and they set Clyde Hooper's house on fire. I hope you two learn a lesson from this." My mother was rarely this excited. "I'm certainly glad you were home when all this happened."

"Mom, where will Mr. Hooper go? I mean, there aren't many ladies like Mrs. Proust who will give him a place to live."

My mother said, "You boys don't understand. It's Sister Proust who will have trouble now. Brother Hooper paid her house payment for her in exchange for living in that little bungalow. He's an artist, a wood-carver who sells his carvings of animals all over the world. He clamps a piece of wood to his workbench and then uses his one good arm to carve these beautiful pieces of sculpture. Oh, he'll find a place to live and work, but I just don't know how Sister Proust will be able to keep her home."

Bill and I went to our bedroom to sort out our trick-or-treat candy. "I'm through with the Simpsons," Bill said. I raised an eyebrow. "Oh, I don't know they were the ones who shoved over the scarecrow, but even if they didn't do it, they could have. I'm through with them."

I dumped my bag of goodies on the floor and began sorting it into piles of jelly beans, popcorn balls, and such. There, amid the candy, was a small, exquisitely carved black cat with its mouth open and its back arched.

Bill began sorting his candy. Hiding among his goodies was a horse chestnut.

CHAPTER 3

♥

*Often love can be expressed more
loudly in actions than in words.*

$\mathcal{T}$he seventh grade is a terrible time in one's life. The only thing that can make it worse is having to go to a new school where you know no one. Tom Stanley faced both challenges in his life when he moved to our community. It could have been easier, too, if Tom hadn't stuck out so clearly in a crowd. Although he had just turned twelve years of age, he looked about nine. He was the shortest and scrawniest seventh-grader in our school. His skin was so pale that it looked translucent, his eyes were a pale powder blue, and his hair was almost white. The only part of Tom Stanley that was twelve-year-old size was his nose, which hung like a hawk's beak on his face.

Warren Grimes, on the other hand, was the biggest kid in our class. There were rumors that Warren had been held back a year or two, but no one dared ask him about it. Warren was nearly six feet tall and over 250 pounds. In contrast to Tom Stanley, Warren was dark-complexioned and had an unruly thatch of black hair that he continually flipped out of his eyes with a jerk of his head. He constantly wore a red bandana around his neck and dared anyone to touch it. It was his badge of honor. I knew of no one who liked Warren Grimes, nor did I know of anyone who dared cross him. Warren was the typical class bully.

The three of us shared first period together with Mr. Blake. Papa Blake, as we all called him behind his back, was our music teacher. He was near retirement, bald-headed and wizened, with rimless glasses and poorly fitting false teeth. His classroom was on the second floor of the school, and his window faced the flagpole. Every morning after the flag was raised, Papa Blake dropped a length of sash cord with a hook on the end of it from his window. The hook was attached to the flagpole halyard, which he then pulled up so the flag could not be tampered with during the day. Apparently in the past someone had taken the flag down and replaced it with some underwear, which had then been run up the flagpole. Papa Blake's morning ritual was to end that kind of nonsense.

Mr. Blake had a unique seating chart. The first day of the semester, each of his students had to sing a solo for him. We all sang the same old spiritual, "Go Down, Moses, Way Down in Egypt's Land." Mr. Blake listened intently and then separated us into sopranos, altos, and tenors. There were two rows in his room representing each of those sections. There rarely any bass singers. The better your voice, the closer to the back of the room you sat. Frightened and embarrassed, I completed my solo and took my appointed front row seat in the alto section. (A year later I would sit on the front row of the bass section, which existed in the eighth-grade classes, although on occasion my voice rocketed back into the upper alto range.) Tom Stanley sat right across the aisle from me in the front seat of one of the soprano rows. Warren Grimes was the only bass. Although Mr. Blake seemed a bit confused as to where to put him, he finally seated Warren in a back-row seat in the tenor section.

I did not look forward to music class. I did not sing well and I had heard little of the music Papa Blake taught us to sing. We not only know what we like, we like what we know. There was one bright spot in first period, however. Gloria Chambers sat immediately behind me. I liked it when Papa Blake handed out sheets of music to the class because then I had license to turn around and look at Gloria while I passed the music to her. She had chestnut hair that hung to her shoulders, green eyes shrouded with long lashes, and the most beautiful pouting red lips I had ever seen. My heart beat with an unspoken love. Once Mr. Blake counted incorrectly and sent an extra sheet of music down our row. When it was sent back up to the front, Gloria put her hand on my shoulder and handed me the piece of paper. I grinned like a baboon when I turned and took the proffered music. I could feel where her hand had touched me. My shoulder stayed warm all day, and my daydreams ran rampant.

Not only did I sit next to Tom Stanley in class, but Mr. Blake assigned us lockers next to each other in the back of the upper hall. Ninth-graders were assigned lockers on the first floor, eighth-graders in the front hallway of the second floor, and seventh-graders the darkest hallway in the school on the back of the second floor. Tom had difficulty getting his combination lock to open. "Mr. Blake," he called out in his thin, reedy voice, "I can't get my lock to work."

Warren had opened his locker, three lockers further down the hall, and was standing nearly hidden behind the open door. "Mommy, Mommy, this is Tommy," he chanted. "Come and help your little guy before he starts to bawl and cry." And as if on command, tears started to roll down Tom's cheeks. He sniffed loudly and wiped his nose with the back of his hand before Mr. Blake reached him and helped him open his lock. Warren chuckled.

When lunchtime came I found myself standing a half-dozen people behind Tom in the lunch line. We pushed our cafeteria trays along the rails where the lunchroom workers handed us our plates of food. At the end of the rail Tom paused to pay for his lunch. As he balanced the tray in one hand and tried to put his change back in his pocket with the other, Warren Grimes bumped into him, sending the metal tray flying. "Watch out, you stupid little jerk," said Warren. Tom stood there mortified. The cashier turned at the sound of the tray hitting the floor.

"Don't just stand there," she said. "Pick it up." Tom knelt beside the tray and tried to retrieve what was left of his lunch. Both the spaghetti and the Jell-O had landed upside down. The roll and butter had skittered halfway across the cafeteria. His peanut butter cookie was nowhere to be seen. Only the carton of milk seemed salvageable. A custodian appeared with a bucket and mop and began cleaning up the mess. Tom, with tears running down his face, ran from the cafeteria.

Warren Grimes began to laugh and then to chant, "Tommy, Tommy, find your mommy." He retrieved the carton of milk from the floor and added it to his own tray of food. "Stupid little kid didn't even take his milk. Wouldn't want it to go to waste."

I did not have the same gym class as Tom and Warren, so I was not a witness to the "baseball incident," as Coach Simmons later called it. Apparently both boys were on the same team. Tom was told to play shortstop, and Warren elected to be pitcher. To be more accurate, they were playing softball, not baseball, but the result was the same. Tom and Warren's team was in the field, and a runner was on first base with two out. The batter hit a high fly into left field, and immediately the runner on first began running. The right fielder dropped the ball, retrieved it, and threw it toward the infield. Warren left the pitcher's mound and started running toward the incoming ball from left field. Tom did not move fast enough, and Warren knocked him to the ground, then tripped and fell on top of him. The ball bounced on by and the runner scored. Warren was infuriated. He began punching Tom in the face. Coach Simmons yelled at him, ran onto the field, and pulled Warren off of Tom.

"Stupid little jerk got in my way. I'll teach him," growled Warren.

"You go into my office and wait for me," commanded Coach Simmons as he spun Warren around and pointed him toward the school. "Are you all right?" he asked Tom as he knelt beside him.

Tears were flowing freely and mixing with the blood from Tom's nose. The rest of the class gathered around. Tom sobbed uncontrollably as he covered his bleeding nose with his hand. Coach Simmons helped him stagger to his feet. "Come with me," he said. "Let's get a cold towel on that. The rest of you boys go on in and shower."

The baseball incident became more graphic and violent with each retelling, but apparently there were no broken bones. Warren's parents were contacted and he was suspended from school for a few days. When he returned, he was apparently unrepentant, because the taunting of Tommy Stanley continued.

Each morning Tom waited until the last possible moment to scramble into first period, apparently hoping Warren Grimes would already be in his seat. Sometimes he was. Often he appeared immediately after Tom and walked down the aisle between us on the way to his back-row seat. Always he bumped into Tom's desk and sent his books and papers flying, or worse. On occasion he would turn to Gloria, ruffle her hair with his hand, and say, "Hi there, good-lookin'." This, of course, infuriated me, but I was too chicken to incur Warren's wrath.

One afternoon in the late autumn I walked out the back door of the school to head home. A large circle of kids had gathered on the lawn immediately to the west of the school. Curious, I joined them. There, in the middle of the circle, were Warren and Tom. Warren had grabbed Tom's arm and had it twisted behind him. "You stupid little jerk," hissed Warren. "Don't you never touch my neckerchief again. You got that?" Tom howled pitifully. "I said, you got that?" Warren spat out as he pushed Tom's arm a little higher. "And another thing. Don't you never talk to my girl again. I seen you sidlin' up to Gloria. You leave her alone. You got that, you stupid little jerk?" Warren threw Tom to the grass and stomped off. Tom remained a sobbing, sodden heap on the grass. The circle of students dispersed. I went to Tom's side and knelt down beside him.

"You all right?"

"Leave me alone," he sobbed. I shrugged my shoulders, stood, and walked home.

The next morning Gloria was in her seat when I took mine. Warren and Tom were nowhere to be seen. I swallowed hard, turned, and asked, "Gloria, are you really Warren's girlfriend?" I checked quickly to see if Warren had entered and seen me talking to her.

Gloria's green eyes blazed. "Of course not. He just thinks he can take anything he wants. Him and his stupid handkerchief."

I turned around, smiling.

Neither Warren nor Tom was there that day. Warren arrived the next day and tousled Gloria's hair on the way to his seat. Tom did not appear. In fact, it was three days before Tom showed up in class, and when he did he had a navy-blue stocking cap jammed on his head and pulled down over his ears. "Hey, Tom, how come you're wearing a cap?" I whispered. He just shrugged his shoulders and looked forlornly at his desk. Mr. Blake did not let us wear hats in class, but he seemed to ignore Tom's.

The next day he arrived wearing the same stocking

cap. Something was obviously peculiar about this. In the middle of class Warren's hand shot up. "Mr. Blake, I gotta go to the bathroom."

Papa Blake peered at Warren. "Oh, all right, Warren, but hurry. We've got to get this music ready for the Christmas program."

Warren stood up from his seat and walked briskly down the aisle between Tom and me to the front of the room. As he passed Tom's desk, his hand flicked out and he pulled the stocking cap from Tom's head. The whole class gasped in unison. I heard Gloria behind me say, "Oh, no, poor Tom." Tom's head had been shaved completely bald and painted bright purple. Tom grabbed his cap from Warren and jammed it back on his head. Then he began to sob quietly. Warren sauntered out of the room.

Mr. Blake walked to Tom's desk and whispered something in his ear. Tom arose, walked to the doorway, and looked warily into the hall, then left the room. Mr. Blake turned to the rest of us, who sat in shocked silence. "Class," he began, clearing his throat, "Tom has been diagnosed with a case of ringworm on his scalp. In order to treat it, the doctor shaves your head and paints it with something called methyl violet. It gets rid of the ringworm, but it won't wash off. It stays on your scalp for nearly a month. Tom has been given permission to wear a stocking cap until the color wears off." He seemed to be searching for the right words. "I don't believe Warren's actions were called for," he said at last. "I wish someone could do something to make Tom feel more accepted." He cleared his throat again and turned back to the music for the program.

Tom was not in school the next day. Gloria entered with a paper bag in her hand. She glowered at Warren as he walked past her on the way to his desk.

"What's you looking at?" Warren growled at me when

he saw me watching him. I turned around and faced forward. I heard the sound of the paper bag being pushed into the open throat of Gloria's desk.

The next day Tom reappeared, stocking cap securely in place and eyes glued to the floor. He avoided looking at anyone as he took his front row seat. The bell rang and Mr. Blake rose to take roll. I heard the sound of a paper bag being extricated from Gloria's desk. And then a broad smile crossed Mr. Blake's face. I turned to see what he was smiling at. Gloria had pulled a stocking cap down on her head. She smiled at Tom.

The next day all of us, including Mr. Blake, wore stocking caps. More accurately, all of us but one, but then, maybe stocking caps and neckerchiefs don't go well together.

CHAPTER 4

♥

*A wise man said, "Keep your
eyes wide open during courtship
and half closed after marriage."*

$\mathcal{G}$reat wisdom is often delivered in small doses.
When I was fourteen years of age my family moved to a
new house—at least, it was new to us. The first Sunday I
attended church I met other young men of the ward who
took me into their circle of friendship and who, today, I
view as lifelong friends.

"Do you like basketball?" I was asked as we walked
home from school the following Friday afternoon.

"Sure. I like it, but I'm not very good at it," I replied
honestly.

"That doesn't matter. We're going up to the church in
the morning. Want to come along?"

In the ward I had moved from there were very tight
rules about using the church gymnasium. You had to
have an adult present, and you had to schedule the time
you wanted to use it at least a week in advance. Most of
us felt it wasn't worth the effort. Some of the older boys
learned how to stick small pebbles against the doorjamb
so that the door wouldn't close tightly, and then they'd
come back to play unannounced and certainly unwel-
comed. Our church custodian, who oversaw the use of

the building, seemed to glory in his power. If and when he caught any unauthorized visitors, it generally meant a visit with the bishop, the parents, and the offenders.

"Did you schedule the building?" I asked with my previous experiences in mind. "Who's coming with us?"

"Oh, just a bunch of the guys are going up to play a little ball. Brother Percy won't mind."

"Who is Brother Percy?" I queried.

"He's the custodian. His real name is Percival— Percival Roberts. He's real cool."

"And he'll just let us in?" I couldn't believe my ears.

"Oh, he'll probably be there cleaning anyway. He never seems to stop cleaning. But if he isn't, he lives in the house next to the church, and he'll let us in or give us a key."

This was unbelievable to me, but the next morning when we arrived at the church, the doors were open. "Brother Percy?" Dale, my next-door neighbor, called out. "Okay if we play a little ball?"

Immediately a little gnome of a man popped out of a classroom. "Sure, me boys. Just remember where you are." Percival Roberts stared at the group of us. "And who's the new chap?" he asked, nodding his head in my direction. He fairly skipped down the hall and grabbed my hand. "I'm Percival Roberts," he said, shaking my hand vigorously, "though most just call me Percy. And who might you be?"

At fourteen years of age—a small fourteen years of age—I looked Brother Roberts square in the eye. His head was covered with a carefully combed thatch of pure white hair. His bright blue eyes twinkled above rosy cheeks. A pair of wire-rimmed spectacles perched on his button nose. And a broad, broad smile covered his face. He was wearing a pair of ancient striped coveralls over what appeared to be red long johns.

I introduced myself while he continued to look in my eyes and pump my hand. "Glad to have you aboard," he said in his broad British accent. "Boys," he said, almost apologetically, "I've got to have you out of here by noon. We've got a ward dinner in here this evening, and the high priests are coming to set up tables at twelve." He nodded toward Dale, who was carrying the basketball. "Now, give me a shot." Dale bounced the basketball toward Brother Percy, who tilted his head and launched the ball toward the basket from the doorway of the gymnasium. The ball fell five feet short of the basket. "I'm getting closer," he laughed as he spun around and whisked down the hallway toward the classroom he'd been cleaning.

We played a spirited game of basketball for the next two hours. No one kept score; we just had fun. Suddenly Brother Percy popped into the gym. "Have to sweep the floor now, me boy-ohs. Whew! And we might want to air the place out a bit." He waved his hand in front of his nose. "But give me one more shot." I bounced the ball to him. He eyed the basket and tried a two-handed set shot from the foul line. This time he actually hit the backboard. "I'm getting better," he chortled.

"Want some help?" Dale asked.

"I never turn down an offer like that. You know what they say—many hands make light work." And Brother Percy handed an enormous dust mop to Dale. In fifteen minutes we had swept the floor and helped Brother Percy set up folding tables and chairs for the ward dinner.

"I thought you said the high priests were coming over to do this," I said.

"They're busy men," said Brother Percy, "and just think what a surprise we have for them when they get here! Thank you for your help."

I never knew whether any high priests showed up, or whether any were supposed to show up. I just knew that things were going to be ready for a ward dinner that night. "He's real nice," I exclaimed later to Dale.

"Yeah, Brother Percy's great. Not much of a basketball player, though. He takes a shot or two every time we're there, and I've never seen him make a basket."

"Does he take care of the building all by himself?" I asked.

Dale's face darkened. "Almost. His wife helps him. Boy, is she different from Brother Percy." There were nods of agreement among the rest of my newfound friends. "If she's there . . . well, sometimes it's just easier to go home."

"How come?"

"Well, she gives us a hard time for being there, and she gives Brother Percy a hard time for letting us in. She's just always . . ." He struggled for the right word. "She's sort of . . . well, you'll meet her soon enough."

Dale was right. The next morning at church, Brother Percy was sitting by the door to the chapel as we entered. He jumped to his feet and extended his hand. "Welcome, me boy-oh, these beautiful people must be the rest of your family. I'm Brother Roberts," he said, shaking each of my family's hands. "And this lovely woman is my wife, Gwynith." He gestured toward the woman who had been sitting, and was still sitting, on the bench next to him. My father extended his hand toward her. She reluctantly took it as if examining a rather unpleasant specimen. She smiled a thin, brittle smile with lips pressed together so hard they left a white ring around her mouth, and inclined her head in the tiniest of nods. My mother's proffered hand received similar treatment. Mine was left dangling in front of her. She merely expelled a quiet huff and turned her head away from me. After an uncomfortable moment I retrieved my hand and found a seat.

The following Saturday a half dozen of us arrived at

the chapel for another game of basketball. Brother Percy bobbed out of a classroom as he heard the door open. "Can we play a little ball, Brother Percy?"

He fairly skipped down the hallway toward the gymnasium. "Only if I get me shot, boy-ohs." He took the proffered basketball and launched it toward the basket. "Another air ball," he said as the ball fell short of the basket. "Ah, well, that leaves me room for improvement. Have fun." He turned and flew down the hallway.

Half an hour later we were sweating profusely, and took a break to get a drink from the fountain in the hall. As I bent over the gleaming stainless steel fountain, I heard the door open behind me.

"Who in the world let you foul urchins in here?" Sister Roberts screamed.

"Uh-oh," said Dale under his breath.

"Why do I even try?" she exploded as she cast her eyes upward at the ceiling and shook her hands above her head. "It isn't enough I work my fingers to the bone cleaning this building every day. Now I have to put up with you smelly little beggars fouling the air the day before the Sabbath." At that moment Brother Percy popped out of a room down the hallway.

"Ah, Gwynith, my sweet. What brings you here today? The boys were just having a friendly game of basketball. No harm done."

"Percival Walkingham Roberts!" she screeched. "I thought we had an understanding. You know the rules as well as I. These boys are not to be here unsupervised. You never know what mischief they'll get into." She shook her finger in Brother Roberts's face.

"Ah, my sweet, they're good chaps. They don't give me any grief, and they often help with me chores." He shrugged his shoulders and his lips formed a half smile.

"We were just going," interjected Dale. "Hope we didn't upset anything." We fairly flew out the door.

"They're sure different," I mused as we walked home. "He's so nice, and she's so . . ."

"Well, my mom says opposites attract," replied Dale.

The next morning at church, Brother and Sister Roberts were again sitting by the back door of the chapel. Apparently it was their ususal spot. "Good morning," Brother Roberts beamed as he leapt to his feet and shook hands with my family. Sister Roberts remained seated with her white-rimmed lips.

"I'm sorry if we caused problems yesterday," I began. Brother Roberts shook his head. His wife sniffed and turned her head away from me.

"No problem, me boy-oh, you're always welcome in the Lord's house."

Sister Roberts's head snapped back as she glared at her husband. The white rim around her lips grew more pronounced. Then, with a shudder, she looked straight ahead toward the pulpit.

Our basketball games continued into the winter months. Brother Percy always greeted us as if we were long-lost friends. He'd take the basketball and try a shot or two, never making a basket; then leave us to play. If his wife appeared, we disappeared.

One Saturday night it began to snow. Dale called me on the telephone just as I was getting ready for bed. "We're going to go help shovel snow around the church early tomorrow morning. Want to come?"

"Sure," I said. "What time?"

"Well, the first meeting's at eight-thirty, so we're going up about seven o'clock."

"I'll be ready."

By seven o'clock there were about ten inches of snow on the ground. Dale and I arrived at the church and found the walks were already shoveled. Brother Percy was just finishing the last sidewalk to the back door when we showed up. "Ah, me boy-ohs, you've come to help, have you? Well, we've got this wee bit of snow to get off the path before the people start arriving. Thrust in your shovels and we'll have it done in a jiffy."

Within five minutes the last bit of snow had been removed. "How early did you have to get up to do this?" I asked.

"I'm an early riser, me boy-ohs. I started shoveling about five o'clock. But I do appreciate your help. I think I'm getting a little older, if not wiser." He chuckled as he waved a mittened hand to us and started next door toward home.

Later that morning as we entered church, Brother Roberts jumped to his feet from his seat near the door. As he pumped my hand he said, "It was a real help, it was, to have you boys help with the snow shoveling this morning."

"Humph," snorted Sister Roberts. "The old fool's going to die from the cold one of these days," she exclaimed to no one in particular.

❤

The winter snows melted and the rebirth of spring brought new challenges to our chapel. Flowers had to be planted and weeds pulled. The trees needed to be pruned, the grass mowed and edged. Brother Roberts was everywhere, it seemed. "You sure work hard," I said one day as we helped plant petunias in the flower beds.

"Ah, it wouldn't be right to have someone think ill of the Lord's house just because old Percy's too lazy to keep it clean, now, would it?" He smiled. "And I do appreciate you boys helping. I know you're busy, too." It seemed like scant payment for the use of the gymnasium all year long. "Besides, who knows when you won't be able to make your little contribution?"

One Sunday late in June, the bishop was conducting

sacrament meeting. "I have a few announcements to make," he began. "The annual Fourth of July breakfast will be held in the parking lot behind the church at seven A.M. We will have a flag raising by the scout troop followed by breakfast. Remember to bring your own plates and utensils." He paused. "This next announcement is a hard one for me to make. I've grown to love Brother Roberts so much . . . and Sister Roberts. He's taken such loving care of this building. But he's decided it's time to retire. Brother and Sister Roberts are going to travel back to their native England on a well-deserved vacation next month. We're going to have a little reception to honor them next Saturday evening. We hope all of you can attend. The reception will be from seven until nine o'clock. There will be light refreshments served."

The entire congregation from both wards that used our building attended the reception. People who had moved away years before returned to wish the Robertses well. The obligatory punch and cookies were served throughout the evening.

Finally the bishop stood and asked Brother and Sister Roberts to come to the stand. "Brother Percy," said the bishop, "you have been a faithful servant of the Lord and of the people of these two wards. You and your wife have made this building the pride of the neighborhood. I'm sure this little remembrance is insufficient to pay you for your tireless efforts over the past twenty-three years, but we'd like to give it to you anyway and hear a word or two from you and your wife." He handed Brother Roberts a gift wrapped in silver paper. Brother Roberts handed it to his wife and whispered something in her ear.

Sister Roberts pursed her lips tightly. She walked to the microphone. The bishop adjusted the microphone stand and lowered the microphone a foot to her height.

"You'll never know the work that's gone into this building," she began. "You've paid Percy for forty hours each week, and he's given at least sixty. He's never taken a vacation in twenty-three years." Her voice was rising in pitch and volume. "I've tried to make the old fool see that he wasn't being paid enough. But he just wouldn't listen. Well, he may be sorry to be leaving this job, but I'm not. I've had to put up with no time off just as he has." She lifted the glittering silver package in her hands. "No sorry little gift is going to make up for the sacrifice we've had to make. I'm sure this isn't what you wanted to hear, but I felt it needed to be said." She walked back to her seat. Total silence enveloped the hall.

Percival Roberts walked to the microphone. It did not have to be adjusted for his height. He ran his fingers through his snow-white thatch. "My dear brothers and sisters," he began. "It has been my privilege for nearly a quarter of a century to help in some small way with this beautiful building. Every Sunday you good people have come here to worship the Lord. I have seen babies blessed, children baptized and confirmed, wedding receptions, and funerals. It has been my pleasure to help prepare a place for those events . . . some filled with joy, some with sorrow. During these years I have had the help of some of the best people in this world. Many of you have helped clean this building, plant flowers, and shovel snow. This service will not go unnoticed, I am sure. I have had the blessing of associating with eight different bishops during my tour of duty. Each of them has been a special, dedicated man. None of them has been perfect, but then, neither am I. If I have been able to make your worship a little easier through any of my poor efforts, then my reward has already been felt. The young men and women who come to play basketball and volleyball are such great young people. They have treated me with such kindness. I cannot remember when a single act of vandalism has happened to this building. Those who were young when we began our labors have grown older. Many have married and begun families of their own. A few have moved back into this very neighborhood.

"Now, none of this could have happened without the help of all of you. But especially I could not have contributed my small piece without the total support of my dear wife, Gwynith."

A murmur went through the crowd, then all was quiet again. "My sweet Gwynith and I have been married for forty-one years. You know, brothers and sisters, I have been blessed so abundantly. One of those great blessings is Gwynith." He paused a moment and removed his spectacles. "I cannot remember once in that forty-one years when Gwynith has ever uttered an unkind word."

The entire congregation stared in disbelief.

"Another of those great blessings is . . . a poor memory."

Sometimes great wisdom is delivered in small doses.

CHAPTER 5

♥

Of all sad words of tongue or pen,
The saddest are these:
"It might have been!"
—John Greenleaf Whittier

The first time I saw Roland he was standing on the steps in front of the library, unable to control his laughter. His laugh was a strange mixture of sounds. It began as if he were trying to keep from laughing, but little explosions erupted from his closed mouth much like the sounds a child makes blowing bubbles through a drinking straw. After a series of these little burbles of noise, Roland continued with a series of wheezes that escaped the corners of his tightly pressed lips. When he could contain the laughter no longer, his mouth flew open, displaying his teeth as he exploded with a loud braying sound. It was startling enough that I stopped and turned around to see what was so funny. That's when I spied his teeth. They were big teeth, very white teeth, with a gap between his upper front incisors.

The laughter continued for several minutes. Tears were running down his cheeks, and yet it appeared as if he alone understood the joke. People moved away from him, apparently embarrassed. I, too, walked away with a shrug of my shoulders and continued on my way to the bookstore. It was the first day of spring quarter at the university, and I needed a legal pad to take notes.

The lecture hall for my chemistry class seated nearly three hundred people. When I entered it through the back door an hour later, most of the seats were taken. I made my way to one of several vacant seats about halfway down the aisle of the amphitheater. Dr. Kagie entered the room a few moments later, leaned against the lab table in the front of the room, and surveyed the class over the tops of his half-moon eyeglasses. "Good morning," he intoned. He flipped through a thick stack of class cards. "I don't think I'll take the time to call the roll. I'm just going to assume that if you are paying your good money to take this class, you'll be here." He lifted the stack of cards and dropped them unceremoniously into an open drawer behind the lab table. As quickly as his three-hundred-pound frame could move, he shuffled to the chalkboard. "I assume you all are here for chemistry," he said as he wrote the course name and number on the chalkboard.

At that moment a door in the front of the room next to the chalkboard opened, and Roland burst into the room. He searched momentarily for a vacant seat, spotted one next to me, and walked briskly to it. "Excuse me," he said as he stepped over my feet and dropped into the seat. "I hope this seat isn't taken." I shook my head.

Dr. Kagie cleared his throat. "Please try to be on time to my class," he said, looking directly at Roland. He then began his lecture for the day on the structure of the atom. As he lectured he paced slowly from one side of the room to the other, stopping periodically in front of one of the unfortunate souls who had occupied the front row. "See?" he'd question as he jabbed the air in front of the startled face with his forefinger.

"He looks like Tweedledum," whispered Roland out of the side of his mouth. I glanced his way as he broke out into an enormous grin. "Except," he continued, "I don't see Tweedledee anywhere."

Dr. Kagie paused in his wandering and looked directly at Roland. "Do you have a question, young man?"

"I was just wondering," said Roland, "did Bohr assemble the halide column before he arranged the inert gases?"

Dr. Kagie looked stunned. "I don't know," he admitted. "Is there some reason you wanted to know?"

"Just curious, what with the enormous oxidizing potential of the halides and the total lack of reactivity with the inert series, you know, just curious."

Dr. Kagie still looked stunned. "I don't see what difference it makes which ones he worked with first." Roland shrugged his shoulders and the professor resumed his pacing.

"Always keep one question in reserve," whispered Roland.

A short time later class ended, and the two of us exited through the rear doors of the auditorium. As we burst into the sunlight, he offered me his hand. "Roland McArthur's my name."

I shook his hand and returned the greeting. "Are you from around here?" I asked.

"Not quite," was his reply. "Looks like Kagie is going to offer us a real challenge," he said, shifting the subject. "A real challenge to stay awake." I nodded my head and turned to walk across campus to my next class. I raised my hand to wave good-bye, when Roland said, "Where are you headed?"

"English."

"So am I," he chortled. "Mind if I walk along?" He fell into step beside me. "This is a beautiful campus," he said, spreading both arms wide. "It's great to be alive on a day like today." The small talk continued until we reached our destination.

"I noticed you in front of the library this morning," I said. "You were laughing at some joke, I think."

"Was I? Can't seem to remember what it was. See you tomorrow," said Roland as I started climbing the stairs to the second floor. He flashed me a toothy grin and ducked into the restroom. The energy he exuded was amazing.

The next day I arrived for chemistry a few minutes before Dr. Kagie made his appearance. Roland was already there and waved to me as I entered the room. He beckoned to me and pointed to the seat next to his. I sat down, and he grinned at me with his Teddy Roosevelt grin. "Hoped you'd make it today."

By the end of the second week of class I knew little more about Roland McArthur, but I'd discovered him to be a pleasant enough fellow. He seemed to consider me a friend, and walked with me daily from chemistry to my next class, but it never went further than that.

The following Saturday evening I had a date with a girl I'd met the previous quarter in a biology class. Becky and I had gone out enough times to be comfortable in each other's presence. We attended a movie and decided to drop into a local ice cream parlor afterward for a root beer float. There was a small crowd waiting to be seated as we walked through the door. We took our place in line, and suddenly Roland leapt to his feet at a back booth and began waving his hands. "We're over here," he called, "over here."

"A friend of yours?" asked Becky.

"Sort of," I responded. We made our way over to Roland's booth. Sitting beside him was one of the most beautiful girls I'd ever seen. The surprises were just beginning.

"Patricia, let me introduce you to my good friend Dick," he said as he extended his hand in my direction. "This is Patricia, my intended. And who is this lovely lady?" he asked, indicating Becky.

"This is Becky. Becky, this is Roland; we sit next to each other in chemistry." We sat down across from Roland and Patricia. Over root beer floats we learned that the two of them were planning to be married in June, just after the end of the school year. In his usual flamboyant manner, Roland described their marriage plans. We listened intently as he talked about how the reception center was to be decorated and the colors they were going to use. He flashed his toothy grin at Patricia and then at the two of us. Patricia sat quietly, barely uttering a word. Suddenly Roland looked at his wristwatch, sprang to his feet, and extended his hand to Patricia to help her from her seat. The evening was obviously ended.

The two of them left in a little sports car. Becky and I climbed into my ancient auto. "He seems really friendly," she said. "His fiancée is kind of quiet, though."

"She didn't have much of a chance, I guess. Roland kind of dominates the conversation."

"She's really pretty. I wonder what attracted her to him." Becky blushed. "I mean, he's not ugly or anything, but he's not really handsome."

"I don't know," I replied. "I really don't know him that well. We just have a class together."

"Well, he's certainly outgoing. And he seems to think you're his friend. By the way, did you notice she wasn't wearing an engagement ring?"

I shook my head. "Not very observant of me, I guess."

The next Monday, Roland was waiting for me in our chemistry class. "How do you like Patricia?" he asked, and then, before I could answer, he continued, "I'm the luckiest guy in the world to have someone like her pay attention to me. What do you think?"

"She's beautiful, Roland. Where did you two meet?" At that moment Dr. Kagie walked through the door and class began.

Before I met Patricia, Roland had never mentioned

her, but for the next three weeks until midterm Roland talked incessantly about Patricia on our walks between classes. He discussed the impending wedding plans. He told me over and over again how lucky he was to have met her and to have her fall in love with him.

"How did you two get together?" I asked him as we walked toward my English class.

Roland gave a contented sigh. "That's why I'm here. I met Patricia last fall at a frat party. I've been dating her ever since. I'm not sure what she sees in me. Did I mention that this weekend we're going to get the invitations printed?"

"Be certain to send me one," I said over my shoulder as I climbed the stairs to my classroom.

"You can count on it," he replied.

The following Monday when I came to chemistry class, Roland did not appear. Nor did he appear the next morning. By Friday I was concerned. I decided to contact him. I realized I didn't know where he lived, nor did I know his phone number. After class I approached the professor. "Dr. Kagie, I don't know if you remember the man who was sitting next to me?"

Dr. Kagie peered over the top of his half-moon glasses. "The boy with the teeth?" I nodded. "Yes, what about him?"

"Well, he's never missed a day of class this quarter until now, and he hasn't been here at all this week. I just wonder if you'd let me get his phone number from his class card. I'm just kind of worried about him. I'm sure it's a little irregular, but I don't know where else to get his number."

Dr. Kagie opened the drawer in the lab table and removed the stack of class cards. "What's his name?"

"McArthur . . . Roland McArthur."

The cards were apparently in alphabetical order. He flipped through them. "McArthur—are you sure about

49

that?" I nodded my head. "Haven't got a card for any-body named McArthur. Sorry."

"Would you look again?" I pleaded. "I mean, he sat next to me for the last five weeks."

"I don't have a card for him," Dr. Kagie said flatly. "Look for yourself if you want." He handed me the stack of cards. I flipped quickly through the stack. He was right. There was no card for Roland McArthur. I thanked him and left.

❤

The quarter finally ended. I received no wedding in-vitation. I saw neither Roland nor Patricia. I saw no wed-ding announcement in the newspaper. It was as if the two of them had disappeared. As the summer pro-gressed, other things pushed Roland from my mind.

In time I met and married my wife . . . it was not Becky. For our fifteenth wedding anniversary we decided to take a short vacation without our six children. We traveled to a little vacation resort an hour from our home. We registered, settled into our room, and left to play a round of golf. It was a leisurely day. We visited the resort restaurant for a lovely candlelight dinner. As we were leaving the dining room, a man dressed in over-alls walked past us with his toolbox in hand. He bumped into my wife.

"Sorry," he said, and smiled at her—a smile filled with big white teeth with a gap between the incisors.

"Roland McArthur!" I exclaimed.

He focused his attention on me, and his brow knit for a moment. Then he snapped his fingers. "Chemistry class," he said. He paused for a moment. "Sorry, I don't remember your name."

I refreshed his memory and introduced my wife to him. Curiosity gnawed at me, but I could not think of a courteous way to ask what had happened to him nearly twenty years before. There was an uncomfortable pause, and then he said, "Well, I have a little job I need to finish." He smiled at my wife. "Nice to have met you." He turned to go, then stopped and looked directly at me. "How long are you going to be here?"

"We'll be here tomorrow, Friday, then we're heading home Saturday morning."

Roland nodded his head and left.

"Where do you know him from?" asked my wife.

"From a long time ago, nearly twenty years." I told her the story as I remembered it. "I'd sure like to know what happened," I concluded.

"Ask him," said my wife.

"Maybe I will, if we bump into him again."

❤

The next morning we were returning from a walk along the edge of the golf course, when Roland emerged from a tool shed. He gave a tentative wave and walked quickly to intercept us. "Good morning," he said, flashing his toothy grin. "I don't want to interrupt anything . . ." He let the sentence hang in the air.

"Just out for a walk," my wife said.

"I wonder . . ." He paused. "I wonder if you have a few minutes to talk?"

"I'll just leave you two alone," said my wife.

"No, no," said Roland, "please stay. This won't take long. I think I owe your husband an explanation for something that happened a long, long time ago." He led us to a bench set back in the trees at the edge of the green carpet of grass. "Please," he said, pointing toward the bench. We sat down.

Roland stood in front of us and gazed across the valley at the mountains beyond. "This is painful, you know," he

finally said. "Something I've tried to forget for years." He
stopped talking for a moment, then spread out his hands.
"Beautiful place. Quiet. Tranquil." I noticed tears were
filling his eyes.

"Listen," I said, "you don't owe me anything. I mean,
if you don't want to talk about it, I understand."

"No, no . . . it's time I put the past behind me." He
reached in the back pocket of his coveralls and removed
a handkerchief. He wiped his eyes and softly blew his
nose. "I don't know how much you remember about
me," he began.

"Not much. You weren't very open about your life.
The last thing I remember is that you and Patricia were
going to get married, and then you just sort of disappeared."

"Patricia. Funny you'd remember her name. If I remember correctly, you only saw her once." I nodded my
head. "Ah, Patricia. Not Pat, not Patty, always Patricia."
He wiped his eyes again.

"I met her at a party. I was trying to get the money
together to attend the university. No one in my family
had ever gone beyond high school, and my folks didn't
see much value in it. Dad owned a farm outside of
Rupert, and he expected me to stay there and help run
the place. I didn't have much interest in farming and,
well, we had quite a fight, and I ended up walking out
of the house and catching the bus to Salt Lake. I've never
been back, you know. My folks are old people now. We
haven't written or talked in years." His voice trailed off.
He looked down at the grass, then smiled through his
tears. "But that's another story, for another time.

"Anyway, I came to Salt Lake and found an inexpen-
sive—no, make that cheap—basement apartment that I
shared with three other guys. I had enough money for
room and board, but not enough to enroll in school. I
found a job—didn't pay much, but enough to pay my

rent and put a little in the bank toward tuition for the next quarter.

"My roommates were all enrolled at the university, and one night they took me to a party. In the course of the evening I met Patricia. I couldn't take my eyes off of her. She was the most beautiful girl I'd ever seen." Tears flowed down his cheeks as twenty years of submerged memories peeled away. "One of my roommates dared me to ask her for a date—you know, one of those dumb things you do when you're twenty years old. At any rate, she accepted my invitation." A deer moved silently through the trees a few yards behind us. Roland quit talking and pointed in her direction.

"Portland," he finally resumed. "Patricia was from Portland. We dated off and on for a couple of months, and then we just quit seeing anyone else. By Christmas break we'd talked about marriage. She went home to visit her family for the holidays, and we agreed we'd celebrate our Christmas when she returned. I'd never been happier in my life." He stopped again and looked across the valley. "I'm taking too much of your time," he blurted.

"Not at all. Please, go on."

"Well, I had a decision to make. I'd saved up enough money for tuition and books for winter quarter, but that was really all the money I had. School or Patricia—it wasn't a very hard decision. I took my tuition money and bought her an engagement ring, a quarter-carat diamond. Actually I could only make the down payment, but I had the ring for Patricia when she returned." Roland stopped and cleared his throat. "You know, I'd never taken her to see where I lived . . . too embarrassed, I guess. I always picked her up at her sorority house. We had a sort of communal car that we four roommates owned." He stopped again and sat down on the grass in front of us. "Patricia came home. She came home driving a brand-new sports car her parents had given her for Christmas. We met to celebrate the holidays. She gave me a pair of gloves, and I remember telling her I had something for her hand, too. I handed her the ring in a pink velvet box."

Roland stared at the grass and plucked a few blades. "We decided to keep our engagement a secret for a while. She needed time to break the news to her parents. I called home to tell my folks, but Dad answered the phone and just hung up on me." Roland looked up at me and tried to flash a smile. "Of course, I couldn't tell Patricia I'd spent my tuition money on her ring, so I pretended I was enrolled and just started attending classes. It doesn't take many brains to figure out that if you attend a class with three hundred students, the professor probably won't call the roll. You can take the tests, but you never turn them in to be graded. No pressure. Of course, you aren't earning any credit toward graduation, but when you're young and in love, you do foolish things.

"Early in April Patricia's parents wanted to meet me. They were driving to a convention in Phoenix and decided to spend the night in Salt Lake. Patricia and I met them for dinner at the Roof restaurant in the Hotel Utah. They were gracious, beautiful people. It was a perfect evening." Roland plucked more grass and threw the blades into the gentle breeze blowing along the hillside. His voice grew very quiet. "I haven't thought about these things in years. It's funny how things twist together, isn't it?

"It was the next night that you saw us in the ice cream parlor. We were celebrating how well the previous evening had gone and starting to plan our wedding. We drove in her car to Patricia's sorority house. She had to be in by eleven. They had very strict rules. We parked her car and walked to the back door. I kissed her good night, and as I turned to go she said, 'Well, old house, I guess I won't be living here much longer.'

"It hit me like a brick. How in the world was I going to be able to provide for a wife? Here I was, a farm boy from Rupert, pretending to go to college and barely able to pay his share of the rent for a basement hovel. As I walked home, my moods shifted from the euphoria of knowing Patricia loved me to the depression of wondering how I could ever support the two of us."

"Did you talk to Patricia about this?" asked my wife.

"How could I? She thought I was a student at the university. I was living a lie, and I knew if she found out the truth it would all be over between us. Besides, I just knew that there was a solution waiting for us—well, for me. I'd found a job that paid more. We started looking for a place to live. Patricia actually had very simple tastes. I really believed we could make it. Then . . ." His voice trailed off.

We waited in silence. Fluffy whipped cream clouds were forming over the mountains to the east. Roland searched the clouds with his eyes.

"Then it happened. We were supposed to meet to pick out wedding invitations after I got off work. Patricia and I had seen each other on campus that morning. I walked with her to the union building. She was very quiet. It's funny how I can remember so clearly after all these years. She told me she had something to tell me before we picked out our invitations. A kind of surprise. I left her and went to chemistry class. You know, I really liked chemistry. I'd always had an interest in science."

We had reached the point in our histories where our paths had parted. I could tell Roland was building up the courage to go on.

"I walked home for lunch. There on the kitchen table was the ring box that I'd given to Patricia. I didn't even think she knew where I lived, and there, sitting on the table, was that pink velvet box." Roland shook his head.

"The ring was inside?" asked my wife.

"Didn't even look. It was obvious that Patricia had found out the truth about me and had decided to break off the engagement. I picked up the box, stuffed it in my coat pocket, and walked to work. On the way I passed a mailbox on the corner. I reached into my pocket and dropped the ring box into it. Just got rid of it. Clean break. Better that way."

"Didn't you try to reach her?" asked my wife.

"What for? It was over. I quit work and went home to my apartment. Gathered my belongings together and went to the bus station. I started home to Rupert before I realized that that door was closed to me as well. I've moved from place to place. Been working here for about five years. Good people. Secluded. Great scenery. The pay's not too bad, and I don't have many expenses."

"And you've never heard from Patricia?" I asked. "You've never tried to contact her in all these years?"

He shook his head.

"Where is she?" asked my wife.

Roland's head came up quickly and he peered into my wife's eyes. "What do you mean?"

"You've never forgotten her, Roland. You can't just have totally turned your back on her. I'll bet you've looked up her address in the phone book. You've driven by her house. You might not have contacted her, but I'm sure you know where she is."

Roland swallowed as if he had a great lump in his throat. "She's still in Salt Lake," he whispered. "Graduated in nursing. Works at the LDS Hospital."

"Married?"

"Not as far as I know." The tears began to fall.

"Write to her, Roland. Call her," my wife pleaded.

He shook his head. "I can't," he sobbed. "I just can't. It has been too many years and too much hurt."

My wife reached out and squeezed his shoulder. She looked at me and indicated with her eyes and a jerk of her head that we should leave. Roland leaned back against the bench and gazed at the mountains as we made our way to the resort.

"Do you remember Patricia's last name?" my wife asked me as we walked away. I shook my head.

❤

Our vacation ended. We did not see any more of Roland before we left for home. A week later my wife was waiting when I returned home from my summer job. "Found her!" she exclaimed.

"Who?" I asked, puzzled.

"Patricia. Patricia Phillips. She's a supervisor in the nursery. She lives by herself in an apartment two blocks from the hospital."

"Congratulations," I said somewhat sarcastically. "What do you plan to do now?"

"We're going visiting. I've called and made an appointment."

"You're out of your mind," I said. "What did you tell her?" My wife just smiled.

We drove to Patricia's apartment. "What in the world are we doing?" I asked as we approached her door.

"I don't know, but there are just some questions I'd like answered."

We heard the doorbell ring and a few moments later the door opened. My mind flew back twenty years. The same beautiful Patricia stood in the doorway. A few streaks of silver hair graced her temples, but there was no doubt it was the same woman. Age had been kind. She stared at me as if trying to recollect where she had seen me before.

"Miss Phillips," said my wife, "may we come in for a few minutes?"

"I guess so." She opened the screen door. "What do you want?"

We entered a tastefully decorated living room. Patricia invited us to sit on the sofa.

"My husband is a voice from your past," began my wife.

Patricia's brow furrowed. "I'm sorry, I don't remember you," she stammered.

"Twenty years ago the two of you met. He was a friend of Roland's." Tears sprang unbidden into Patricia's eyes. "Although I believe the two of you met only once."

Patricia stared at me even more intently through her tears. "I'm afraid I still don't remember," she said, slowly shaking her head.

"We don't want to pry into your past, Miss Phillips, but I wonder if I can ask you one question?"

Patricia shrugged her shoulders slightly and nodded her head.

"Why did you decide to break off your engagement with Roland? Why did you return the ring?" asked my wife.

Patricia Phillips's mouth dropped open. She stared at my wife. "I didn't break off the engagement. He did. He just disappeared," she said quietly, regaining her composure.

"But you returned the engagement ring," I said.

"I did what?" She reached for a thin gold chain that hung around her neck and withdrew a ring from within her bodice. She dangled the ring on the end of the chain. "I most certainly did not."

"But the ring box was left on Roland's table," I said. "I'm confused."

"There was a wedding band for him in it. I thought it would be romantic to give his ring to him in the same box in which he gave mine to me."

"But how did it get on his kitchen table? You didn't even know where he lived," I sputtered.

Patricia smiled a gentle, soft smile. "Of course I knew where he lived." She cast her eyes toward the carpet as if the secret were too hard to admit. "I followed him home. He was so secretive about where he lived. I think he was embarrassed about living in that terrible basement apartment. So I just followed him home one night when he left my sorority house. I wanted to surprise him, so I just put the ring in the box and left it on his table." Her eyes clouded. "He was supposed to meet me that afternoon to pick out wedding invitations. But he never showed up. At first I thought something had come up at work. I tried to call him, but no one answered. I went to his apartment the next day, but he had gone. So many unanswered questions." Patricia studied her fingernails, then slid the gold chain from around her neck.

"He spent his tuition money to buy me this ring." She swung it hypnotically back and forth on its golden chain. "No wonder he started to resent me. That was the surprise I had for him that day. Dad and Mom were giving us money for a wedding gift. Enough to pay both our tuitions for the coming year. Maybe he knew that. He was a proud man. Maybe that's why Roland left."

"Well, thank you," said my wife. "We really need to be going."

Patricia stood and opened the door for us. "Why did you ask after all these years? Do you know where Roland is?"

I started to answer, but my wife said, "We just needed to know the answers to some unanswered questions."

We hurried home. My wife dialed the resort. "May I speak to Roland McArthur, please?" There was a pause. "I see. Do you know where he was going? Thank you." She hung up. Tears formed in her eyes. "He's moved on," was all she said.

CHAPTER 6

♥

Jealousy is always born
together with love.
—François, Duc de La Rochefoucauld

$\mathcal{S}$ean was two and a half years old when Kelly was born. But by the time Kelly was eight years old, they looked like twins. It wasn't so much that Sean was short as it was that Kelly was tall for his age. Sean was quite relieved when he entered junior high and no longer attended the same school as his fifth-grade brother.

For two blissful years none of his teachers asked him if Kelly was his twin. It helped further that Sean's junior high school began an hour earlier than Kelly's school, so the two of them didn't even walk to school together.

Of course, the family was a different matter. According to Sean, their Aunt Rhoda could be counted on to go through the same ritual every time she visited. "You two boys stand back to back," she'd warble. "Let's see if Kelly has caught up to Sean." The two of them would accordingly stand back to back, and their Aunt Rhoda would place her hand on top of their heads. "Not yet, Kelly, not yet. Sean still has you by half an inch."

The ritual never changed until the summer before Kelly entered junior high. "Stand back to back," Aunt Rhoda commanded. "Well, Kelly baby, I do believe you're taller than your big brother."

During the school year Kelly continued his growth spurt so that by the end of the year he was nearly an inch taller than Sean. Sean became depressed. The two brothers had always bickered with each other, but now it increased. Sean was jealous. Solace was but a summer away; then he'd attend high school and get away from his pesky little . . . no, make that his pesky younger brother.

I'd known the family for nearly twenty years. I'd watched the two boys grow up and had been as un-thinking as anyone else when I commented on their rela-tive sizes. That fall when Sean entered high school he ended up in my biology class. He had grown to a re-spectable height just shy of six feet. His eighth-grade brother, however, was nearly three inches taller. The only part of Sean that had kept up with Kelly's growth was his feet. Both boys wore size twelve shoes.

When basketball season began I was pleased to see Sean on the sophomore team. He was not a brilliant player, but he was steady. He could handle the ball well, and although he rarely took a shot, his assists were re-sponsible for a number of baskets. Although my assign-ment was to videotape the varsity games for the basket-ball coach, I often arrived early enough to watch the sophomore games. They finished the season with a win-ning record. By the end of the year Sean had grown an-other half inch and seemed to have reached his full height.

That same year Kelly was the star of the eighth-grade team. Not only was he taller than any player on the op-posing teams, he was well coordinated and had a devas-tating jump shot. He intimidated the other teams with his size and ability. Our local paper ran a story about Kelly on the front page of the sports section. The local sports reporter, who is known to exaggerate on occasion, sug-gested that Kelly was at least college material, if not a potential NBA first-round draft choice. Sean was jealous. Kelly's ego was inflated. They barely had a kind word to say to each other.

The next year didn't improve the situation. Sean tried out for the basketball team and made it, but as a junior he spent most of the time on the bench. Our team had a winning record, but only in the final minute of a game that was clearly out of reach did Sean have an opportunity to play. When the team went to the state tournament, Sean's total playing time in four games was forty-one seconds. He attempted one basket, which he missed. He did have an assist during his brief time on the court.

Kelly's ninth-grade team went undefeated. Kelly scored twenty-two points and blocked six shots in the district championship game. He was the hero of the school. The local newspaper ran a picture on the front page of him making a short hook shot. "An Irresistible Force," blared the headline. He was presented with a framed photograph of himself at a school assembly where he was named most valuable player, as well as athlete of the week by the newspaper.

Kelly hung the photograph on the wall opposite the front door of their home, so that anyone entering would see it. He placed his most-valuable-player trophy on the table beneath the photograph. Sean began using the back door so he wouldn't have to see Kelly's shrine. He was extremely jealous. The two brothers rarely spoke to each other, and when they did, acid hung in the air between them.

Sean became a starter on the basketball team during his senior year. He was slightly over six feet, and a good ball handler. He valued his starting position. Kelly began the preseason as the center on the sophomore team. With one preseason game to go, Kelly appeared on the bench with the varsity team. Still Sean was not worried. The team had a senior center who was an inch taller than his brother, and a good player. The chance that Kelly would get into a game seemed slim. In fact, it seemed to Sean that he'd be on the court playing and his brother would have to sit on the bench watching. It felt good.

As the season progressed, it was obvious that our team was the team to beat. Sean had played in every game. He was averaging just over four points and nearly eight assists per game. Kelly had played a few minutes in several of the games. It was clear he was able to take the ball to the hoop, but the senior center had more experience. With one game to go in the regular season, our team had won every game but one. For our final game we were to play the only team that had beaten us. Since our opponent had lost one game as well, the team that won the contest would enter the state tournament as the first-place team from our region.

The game was played in our gymnasium, but there was little home court advantage since the opposing team brought equally as many fans. We were seated on the south, they on the north. The place was packed, the noise level deafening.

At the end of the first quarter the two teams had battled to a tie—eighteen points each. The opposing team played a full-court press at the beginning of the second quarter. Sean broke the press time and time again until their coach abandoned it. At halftime our home team was leading by three points. Both teams had played their starting five for the entire half. Ten totally fatigued young men went to the locker rooms with their team-mates.

During halftime the drill team and pep band performed. The cheerleaders whipped up the already frothing crowd. "Let's bring them back out," they screamed as the teams returned to the court. The crowd responded with a deafening roar.

Both teams slowed down the pace during the third quarter. Each tried to move the ball around to get high percentage shots. The teams traded baskets back and forth, and at the end of the third quarter we led by a single point.

"We're going to do it, men," the coach encouraged. "Sean, you're doing a great job. Just keep feeding that ball to the open man." Sean nodded his agreement. The horn blew and the fourth quarter began.

As the ball was thrown in to start the quarter, an opposing player stole it and raced the length of the court for a lay-up. The fans in the north bleachers screamed their approval. Sean calmly brought the ball down the court. He dribbled the ball toward the right angle of the court. The center broke loose from his man, took three steps from the right side of the lane to the left, and leapt in the air. Sean fired the ball to him and he drilled the ball through the hoop. Now the fans in the south bleachers erupted in screams.

Down the court they raced. The opposing forward shot a short jumper that bounced straight up off the rim. Both centers leapt for the rebound and crashed into each other, falling to the floor. No whistle blew. The ball bounced out of bounds. There was a collective "Ooh" from the crowd. The opposing center got back on his feet and, in a gesture of sportsmanship, reached his hand down to our center. Our player tried to stand, but it was obvious he had sprained his left ankle. Time-out was called, and he was helped from the court. The team doctor examined his ankle and put an ice pack on it. The doctor looked at the coach and shook his head. A moan of dismay went through the south bleachers.

Our coach looked down the row of chairs and beckoned to Kelly. Sean felt a knot in the pit of his stomach. "Men," said the coach, "we can still do it. We're up by a point, and we all know this is not a one-man team. Now, get in there and let's put this one away."

Kelly checked in at the scorekeeper's table and entered the game. The other team threw in the ball. Carefully they worked it around the perimeter until their center pivoted free. The ball was fired into him and he turned to shoot. As the ball left his hand, Kelly swatted it away from the basket. The crowd roared. Sean fought for the ball and came away with it. He drove down the court to the top of the key. He was in the clear. He launched a shot toward the basket. The ball bounced off the back of the rim, and at that moment Kelly arrived in full stride, grabbed the rebound, jumped, and put the ball in the basket. We were ahead by three points.

Kelly sprinted down the court and positioned himself at the left side of the lane just in time to see their point guard shoot a jumper from near the top of the key. The ball swished through the net. He grabbed the ball, stepped out of bounds, and saw his brother waiting for the ball. A man was just behind him ready to steal the ball. The other guard was further down the court. Kelly threw the ball to him.

Sean was fuming. His brother wouldn't even throw him the ball! Down the court they came. The ball was thrown to Sean. His brother cut toward the basket. For one brief moment Sean hesitated, then he threw the ball to his younger brother, who laid the ball up for two points. The game continued. The lead switched back and forth.

They were down by one point with sixty-three seconds left in the game when the coach called a time-out. "Men," he said, "we've got one minute to prove ourselves." The boys listened intently. "Kelly, you've done a great job in the center. If it weren't for you we wouldn't still be in this game."

The little boy in Sean wanted to call out, *What about me? I've been getting him the ball so he could score. How great do you think he'd be without the rest of us?* But in one maturing moment of truth, he realized the coach was right. Without his younger brother's efforts, they would not be winning this game.

The coach outlined the play he wanted run and they were about to go back on the court, when Sean noticed the sole of Kelly's right shoe. It was beginning to peel off from the toe of the shoe. As they walked back on the court, Sean could see the first inch or so of Kelly's sole flip-flopping loose.

Sean took the inbound pass and began to set up the play. Seconds ticked off the clock until finally he was able to thread a pass to the forward, who spun around and launched a shot at the basket. The ball banged off the side of the rim. Kelly leapt for the rebound, grabbed it, came down, and went back up to stuff the ball home. He came back down with his foot sticking half out of his shoe. He tried to run down the court, but his shoe wouldn't let him. The other team took advantage of the situation and regained the lead with sixteen seconds left. As Kelly struggled to get his foot and shoe put back together, his older brother brought the ball down the court. He looked back at Kelly, who was sitting on the floor working with his shoe. Suddenly Sean let out a cry and fell to the floor. Protecting the ball, he signaled a time-out and then grabbed his leg and began massaging it as he rolled around on the floor in obvious agony. The team doctor ran onto the court for the second time that night. He and the coach picked up Sean and carried him to his seat.

The team gathered around while the doctor massaged Sean's right calf. The doctor pulled off Sean's shoe and pushed his toes back toward his shin while he manipulated the calf muscles. Sean moaned in obvious pain. He reached down, retrieved his shoe, and handed it to Kelly. "Put it on," he said through clenched teeth. "At least one of us ought to be in the game." Kelly pulled off his damaged shoe and laced on Sean's.

The whistle blew and the game continued. Twelve seconds showed on the clock. We were down by one point. Ten seconds later, Sean's replacement threw the ball to Kelly, who banked in the winning shot. A desperation court-long shot by our opponents fell short.

If I had not videotaped the game, I probably would have missed the miraculous healing of Sean's muscle spasm. But on instant replay he's there with the rest of the team, leaping up and down, wearing a single shoe.

CHAPTER 7

♥

I sometimes hold it half a sin
To put in words the grief I feel;
For words, like Nature, half reveal
And half conceal the Soul within.
—Alfred, Lord Tennyson

*P*lay golf?" asked the man who was helping me screed the concrete in my driveway.

"What?" I said as the sweat dripped from my forehead onto my eyeglasses.

Slish, slish, went the two-by-four back and forth over the wet concrete, leveling it. "I said, do you play golf?"

"Not very well," I admitted. "But I like to play."

"Good." *Slish, slish.* "We have a ward tournament next Saturday. Shall I sign you up?"

I thought of all the things that had to happen before we could move into our new house. Giving up part of Saturday didn't seem possible. "I've got to get moved in," I finally said. "Maybe next time."

Slish, slish. "Got to take time to smell the fairways too," he said.

We reached the end of the driveway and stood up. I kneaded my back.

"It's true, you know," he said. "Just say the word *concrete* and the sweat starts to pour."

"Thanks so much for your help." I shook his hand. "I'm sorry, though, I've met so many people today I've forgotten your name."

"Paul Jackson," he replied. "Live in the house down the street, the brown one. Sure I can't sign you up for the golf tournament? Nothing like a bunch of big pills chasing little pills all over the course." He chuckled.

"I'd really like to, but we've got to move out of our other house by Monday of next week. I'm afraid this Saturday's going to be pretty busy." I picked up the float to start smoothing the concrete. "Is this a one-time event, or do you have more than one tournament each year?"

Paul chuckled. "I organize one every chance I get. Golf is what keeps me alive. We'll get you next time around." He slipped the cap off his head of close-cropped steel-wool hair and ran a handkerchief over his forehead. "Well, got to get home and pick up my clubs. I've got a tee time in less than an hour." He waved farewell and jogged down the street.

I finished smoothing the driveway with the float and sought some shade and a cool drink under our neighbor's horse chestnut trees. This good man, from whom we'd bought our lot, was waiting with a pitcher of lemonade. "Boy, I certainly appreciate all the help today," I said. Nearly a dozen men from our new ward had spent the morning helping form and level the base for the driveway and sidewalk of our new home. Many had stayed around to help when the concrete trucks arrived. "I really appreciated Paul Jackson's help screeding the driveway. He seems like a really fine man."

"He's very, very nice. And he's a real golf nut. If he can't get a foursome together, he goes into depression. He must play four or five rounds a week."

"He invited me to play in a tournament this weekend, but I've just got to get moved in."

"Oh, he'll make sure you get to play. If you've told him you like to play, he won't forget."

"He must be a good golfer," I said as I drained the glass of lemonade.

"I don't know. I don't play, but he's only been playing for a couple of years. He had a heart attack two or three years ago. It forced him into early retirement, and he's taken up golf for the exercise. Here, have some more lemonade."

❤

By late Saturday night, all of the furniture was moved into our home. Only a few boxes and odds and ends remained in our old house. We collapsed on our bed.

Sunday morning came early, and church started at nine o'clock. Sleepy and sore, we arrived at the chapel. Paul and Ann Jackson were waiting in the foyer. "Sorry we missed you at the tournament," he said, extending his hand. "Putting one together for a week from next Saturday. Interested?"

"Tournament?" said my wife. "What kind of tournament?"

"Golf, of course. Ain't any other kind, is there?" he said, smiling.

My wife grinned at me. "Sign us both up—that is, if the women are allowed to play."

"Absolutely," said Ann. "Consider it done. Who knows, you might win a trophy."

"Trophy?" I said.

"Incredible but true," Paul chortled. "By the way, you don't happen to have any old trophies around your house that you want to get rid of? I have a friend who engraves brass plates for me and we're able to recycle them." We'd reached the door of the chapel, and Paul began introducing us to everyone we met.

Two weeks later we played in our first golf tournament sponsored and organized by Paul Jackson. Following eighteen holes of golf, we retired to Paul's backyard, with nearly a dozen couples who had played in the tournament, for a potluck dinner. Following dinner Paul began distributing trophies. My wife received one for the lowest women's score. I received one inscribed "Most Improved Golfer." Everyone received a trophy. My wife's had a tennis player on top of it. Mine had the "Winged Victory." I slipped the brass plate out of the holder and discovered that the back had been engraved with "3rd Place, Lincoln-Douglas Debate."

❤

Two weeks passed and school began. One reason for building our new home was that it was less than ten minutes from the school where I taught. Our old house was forty-five minutes away. As I was leaving for school, my wife said, "Any chance you can get away by four o'clock? I reserved a tee time, if you're interested in nine holes this afternoon."

❤

After paying our green fee, we walked out of the clubhouse and saw Paul Jackson on the putting green. I called out to him and waved. He waved back. The loudspeaker on the clubhouse blared out, "Jackson party is up, Earl party on deck." A small, dark-haired man dressed in bright green trousers and a fluorescent pink golf cap joined Paul on the first tee.

"Wonder who that is," I said. "I don't remember seeing him before." Several times as we moved around the course we passed Paul moving in the other direction. I got a better look at his partner and was sure I'd never seen him before.

♥

Sunday at church, Paul put his arm around my shoulders. "You had some really good drives Thursday. I'm impressed."

"You know what they say, 'Get one good drive and it will bring you back for another game.'" I thanked him for his compliment. "Who was your partner? He looked like an interesting guy."

A huge smile split Paul's face. "He's the guy who taught me to play golf. He's my dentist. After I had my heart attack, Murray got me out on the links and taught me how to play. We used to have to play in the early morning before he went to his office, but last year he retired, so we can play anytime we want. We usually play three or four times a week. I owe that guy my life."

♥

It seemed that every time my wife and I went to play golf for the rest of the year until the snow flew, we'd see Paul and Murray at the golf course. After winter set in, Paul and his wife spent three weeks in Phoenix after Christmas. Murray and his wife went with them. A week after they returned home, they left for St. George for two weeks.

Their relationship continued for the next ten years. During that time I accumulated trophies for the "Closest to the Hole on the 9th Green" and "First Place Mixed Doubles," among others. As the winter snows melted and the spring flowers burst forth, Paul and Murray anticipated another year of golf. It was not to be.

I was pruning the winter-killed canes from my roses one afternoon, when an ambulance raced down the street, siren screaming and lights flashing. It pulled into the Jacksons' driveway. I put down my pruning shears and started down the street. I reached his home just in time to see Paul Jackson being wheeled out on a stretcher. The ambulance doors were slammed shut and the ambulance shrieked out of the driveway toward the hospital.

Ann's eyes were wet with tears. "Can I drive you to the hospital?" I volunteered. She nodded her head. "I'll run up the street and get the car. I'll be right back." I ran to our house, grabbed the keys to the car, yelled to my wife what was happening, and drove quickly to the Jacksons' home. Ann was waiting.

"Heart attack," she said as I opened the door for her. "Worse than his first one, I'm afraid." She tried to maintain her composure, but once in the car, she buried her face in her hands and wept. I drove as quickly as I could to the hospital. "It just hit him," she said through her tears. "He was just sitting there watching television and it hit him." I nodded my head in sympathy.

We parked the car and hurried into the emergency room. Paul was nowhere to be seen. "We're looking for Paul Jackson," I said at the receptionist's desk. "He should have been brought in just a few minutes ago with a heart attack."

"Have a seat," the receptionist said. "He's in the cardiac care unit. The doctor's with him now. We'll let you know as soon as we know anything."

Ann sat down in front of the large aquarium in the waiting room. "Would you like me to wait with you?" I asked.

She shook her head. "Thank you. No, you go on home. I'll call as soon as I know anything."

"Can I call anyone for you? Your children? Anyone?"

She shook her head. "Thank you. I'll call our son, Little Paul. Thank you for the ride."

"Call me when you're ready to come home and we'll pick you up, okay?"

She nodded. "We'll see," she said quietly. I gave her a little hug and turned to go, when Murray burst through the doors. He spotted us and raced to Ann's side.

"How is he?" he gasped.

"We don't know, Murray. We just got here. He's somewhere in cardiac something-or-other," she blurted. She burst into a fresh fountain of tears and hugged Murray tightly. He put his arms around her and patted her back.

I could see Ann was in good hands, so I shook Murray's hand and left.

"How is he?" asked my wife when I walked into the house.

"Ann says it's worse than his first heart attack, but I really don't know. He's in the hospital and they're working on him."

"Ann shouldn't be there alone," my wife said. "Why don't I go over and sit with her."

"Murray's there," I said. "I'm sure he's going to stay until they know something, and Ann promised to call us as soon as she has any word."

Feeling helpless, I collected my thoughts and went back into the garden and continued pruning the roses. *What a good man Paul is,* I thought. *I hope he recovers quickly.*

Within an hour, the phone rang. "It's Ann," my wife called out the window.

I went into the house and picked up the phone. "Hello, Ann."

"He's gone," she said. I could hear her taking in quick little gulps of air. "Just like that, he's gone." The sobbing began in earnest.

No matter the circumstances, there never seems to be the right thing to say at a time like this. "I'm sorry, Ann, so sorry," was all I could think of at the minute. "We'll be right over." I washed my hands, and my wife and I drove quickly to the emergency room. As we hurried through the doors, my wife spied Ann and hurried to her side. They hugged each other. I spotted Murray staring at the fish in the aquarium. I sat down beside him.

"He was gold. There was no one better than Paul." Murray shook his head slightly back and forth. "He was the brother I never had. He was gold." The tears streamed down his cheeks. I helped him to his feet and put my arms around him. He buried his face against my chest and wept.

❤

During the next two days Ann and Little Paul made the funeral arrangements. Paul's obituary appeared in the local papers. The night before the funeral, a viewing was scheduled at the mortuary from seven o'clock until nine. My wife and I arrived about ten minutes before seven. The line of people attending the viewing already extended into the parking lot. It took nearly forty minutes until we entered the room where Paul's body lay in a beautiful oak casket. A reception line of sorts preceded the casket. Paul's brothers and sisters stood red-eyed at the beginning of the line. Little Paul and Ann stood at the foot of the casket. The room was filled with flower arrangements. "This is quite a tribute to Paul and his family," I said, indicating all of the floral displays and the number of people who had come to honor him.

I spotted Murray and his wife standing by themselves in a corner of the room, almost hidden by the flowers. He was dressed in a black suit, and his wife in a black dress. I noticed he was wearing a yarmulke on his head. They looked somewhat uncomfortable. "There's Murray," I said to my wife. "Keep my place in line, I'm just going to say hello to him."

"How are you doing?" I asked as I shook his hand.

"I'm all right," he said, "and you?"

"Fine, Murray. You were a good friend to Paul. You know, he credited you with saving his life."

A fleeting smile crossed Murray's lips. "How could I have saved his life?"

"By teaching him to play golf. By golfing with him and making him exercise. He really loved you, Murray."

A hint of tears formed in the corners of his eyes. "My friend," he said, "could I ask you a question?"

"Of course."

"I'm not very familiar with these Mormon funerals. I've never seen so many people." He waved his hand toward the line of friends who were offering condolences and strength to Ann. "What happens tomorrow? I understand they will have another viewing at the church, but will the coffin be open as it is tonight? Or will they close it tonight?"

"No, it will be open tomorrow. Probably the viewing will be in the Relief Society room at the chapel. There are two doors into that room, and the line will come in one door and leave through the other. Then, about ten minutes before the funeral service begins, they'll invite just the family to stay in the room. They'll have a family prayer, and anyone who wants to say their final good-byes can before they close the coffin. Then they'll wheel it into the chapel for the actual service." Murray's head nodded up and down. "Does that answer your question?"

"Yes, yes, thank you, my friend." He and his wife started to leave. I noticed Murray walked with a strange gait. It appeared he had injured his left leg, because he kept it straight as they walked from the room. I returned to my wife's side and continued through the line.

The next morning at the chapel was a repeat of the previous night. Hundreds of people came to walk through the line and extend their comfort to Paul's family. Murray and his wife again were standing unobtrusively in one corner of the Relief Society room. I shook Ann's hand. "Anything we can do, you call on us."

She nodded her head. "You've been so helpful. Please stay for the family prayer."

"I'd be pleased," I said.

The appointed moment came. People still in line were encouraged to go directly to the chapel. The Relief Society room was cleared except for family and a few invited friends. Murray and his wife remained in the corner. Paul's brother offered a beautiful family prayer, and the mortician asked if anyone wanted to visit the casket before it was closed.

Little Paul approached the casket. He smiled one last time at his father and patted his hands. Ann bent down and kissed him good-bye. Paul's brothers and sisters filed by.

"Anyone else?" The mortician looked around the room. He began to make the final adjustments with the lining, when Murray moved to the casket with his strange, stiff-legged walk. He looked at the serene face of Paul Jackson, and then he reached into the pocket of his black coat and removed a bright orange golf ball and a tee. He gently lifted Paul's hand and placed the golf ball in the unyielding fingers. He then slipped the tee between two fingers of the other hand.

The mortician looked slightly alarmed. Ann reached out and touched his arm. "It's okay," she nodded.

Murray reached inside his waistband and withdrew a golf club from his left pant leg. He gently and lovingly laid the putter alongside Paul's body. Murray smiled at his friend. The lid of the coffin was closed.

CHAPTER 8

❤

Judge not, and ye shall not
be judged: condemn not, and
ye shall not be condemned:
forgive, and ye shall be forgiven.
—Luke 6:37

$\mathcal{T}$here are no assigned seats in the chapels of The Church of Jesus Christ of Latter-day Saints, but there might just as well be. Each family seems to find a comfortable niche, and on a typical Sunday they migrate to their spots just like the swallows returning to Capistrano. One advantage to this arrangement is that the bishop of the ward can pretty well tell whether a family is in attendance by just looking at their usual location.

One wintery Sunday while serving as bishop, I surveyed the congregation as I sat on the stand listening to the prelude music, finding most of the families in their usual places. However, when I stood up to begin conducting the meeting I noticed a person I didn't recognize sitting on the very front row directly in front of the pulpit. She was a strikingly pretty blonde woman who appeared to be in her early twenties. Sitting next to her was a little boy, about three years of age. The woman glanced up and saw me looking at her. Her eyes immediately dropped to the carpet in front of her. I greeted the congregation, and sacrament meeting began.

When I was seated the pulpit hid the two newcomers from my view, but every time I stood up to announce speakers or musical numbers I found my gaze wandering down to these two souls sitting by themselves on the front row. When the meeting was over I made my way down from the stand just in time to see the young woman, child in tow, heading out the back doors of the chapel. I met with my counselors a few minutes later and asked them if they were aware of anyone moving into the ward. Neither of them was. It was not unusual for people to move into our ward, but we usually knew when they were moving in and supplied help if needed.

❤

On Tuesday we held our weekly youth activity night. That evening the Explorer Scouts were scheduled to visit a local computer company as part of their career exploration activities. The Explorer post adviser had arranged for the visit, and I was planning to go with them. As we were leaving the chapel after opening exercises, I noticed the same young lady sitting on the couch in the foyer of the church. I walked over to her and extended my hand. She stood up and shook my hand. I noticed that she continued to look past me at the announcement board.

"Hi," I said, "are you a new member of the ward? I'm the bishop."

"I know who you are," she said quietly. "I was here for church on Sunday. My name's Becky Butler."

"I saw you. Where are you living?" She paused a moment and then told me she was living in a basement apartment in our ward. "We'd have been happy to have helped you move in. I'm sorry we didn't know you were coming," I said to her.

She still looked past me at the wall. "Bishop, I need to have an interview with you," she finally said.

"That would be just fine." I started to give her the name of my executive secretary to have him set up an appointment, but the Spirit whispered, *Do it now.*

"Do you have time this evening?" I asked. She looked nervous but nodded her head. "Step into my office, please." I opened the door, turned on the light, and said, "I'll be right back."

My ward clerk was working on membership records in the clerk's office, which was adjacent to the bishop's office. I stuck my head in and said, "I have an impromptu interview. Would you mind working on records until I'm through?" He agreed.

Our Explorer adviser came up to me. "New member of the ward?"

"Yes, and she apparently needs some help. Can you take the boys to the computer company without me?" He agreed and left with them.

I went into my office. Becky Butler was standing, looking at a painting of the Savior that was on the wall next to my desk. Tears were running down her face.

"Please," I said, gesturing toward a chair in front of the desk, "have a seat." Her eyes never left the painting as she moved slowly to the chair and sat down.

Listen, whispered the Spirit. I sat in my chair behind the desk and waited.

"Bishop," she began after a pause, "you may not want me in your ward." The tears continued to flow. I handed her a box of tissues. "I don't really know where to begin, but I think you deserve to know my story before you welcome me into the congregation."

I started to speak, but the Spirit whispered, *Just listen for a while.*

Becky Butler shifted her gaze from the Savior to me. "I was born when my parents were quite old. Daddy turned fifty that year and Mom was forty-five. I was their only child. I think I had a pretty normal childhood. I went to school . . . I liked school. But one night when I was about eight years old, I heard my mom and daddy having a terrible argument. Daddy slapped Mom and knocked her right through the screen door and down the front steps. She twisted her arm when she hit the sidewalk, and broke her wrist. The neighbors called the police, who came and took Mom to the hospital in an ambulance and took Daddy to jail to spend the night. I spent the night with our next-door neighbor. Bishop, I was terrified.

"When Mom came home from the hospital the next morning, Daddy came home from jail and was so kind to her. He begged her to forgive him and promised he'd never do anything like that again. He hugged me and told me he loved me and that he loved Mom and that it was liquor that made him mean. He promised he'd quit drinking. Then Mom told him it was her fault. She'd made him mad and she knew he couldn't control himself when he got drunk. The two of them sat on the couch and held each other and cried. I wanted to believe Daddy, but somehow I knew it was going to happen again.

"Daddy was pretty good for nearly a year. Then my mom's mother—we just called her 'Granny'—came to visit. Daddy and Granny didn't get along very well, and one night he came home drunk and started yelling at Granny. Mom tried to calm things down, but Daddy shoved her onto the couch and kept screaming at Granny. Well, Granny had a cane in her hand 'cause she had a bad hip, and when Daddy gave her a little push, she whacked him on the side of his head with her cane. That only made Daddy madder, and he shoved Granny onto the couch. Mom jumped up and grabbed the cane and kept hitting Daddy until he ran out the front door. 'Just like *your* daddy,' said Granny. I was scared to death.

"The next morning Daddy came home with bruises

all over his face. He cried and cried and begged Mom and Granny to forgive him. He promised he'd never touch another drop of liquor. Granny said she didn't trust him and that Grandpa had beaten her until she'd finally thrown him out. She thought Mom ought to do the same thing with Daddy. Anyway, they cried and cried and finally Mom forgave Daddy and Granny left to go home.

"About the time I turned twelve Daddy started beating me along with Mom. He'd get drunk and come home and I'd try to protect Mom; I was almost as big as she was and a lot younger. Daddy slapped me and called me an ungrateful child and told me that if I didn't like the way he was raising me I could go find somewhere else to live. Then Mom would scream at him and tell him he was the one who was going to have to leave, not me.

"Oh, Bishop, I'm just rambling, I'm taking too much of your time."

"Not at all, Sister Butler, not at all," I replied. *Listen,* said the Spirit.

"'Sister Butler,'" she repeated, moving her mouth as if she were tasting the words. "You don't know how good that sounds." She looked past me at the painting of the Savior and then started again. "When I was thirteen Daddy lost his job. He'd sit around the house most of the day and then he'd go out with the boys at night. All day long Mom and I walked on eggshells. If we made too much noise Daddy yelled at us. Nothing I did was done right. It was not a happy time in my life. I'd never had many friends. I mean, Daddy never let me bring anyone home to our house and I was kind of timid anyway. So I was home all the time. When school started that fall I started staying after school as late as I could. It was my way of staying out of Daddy's way. Well, one day I was in the library doing my homework and this boy came over to the table where I was sitting. He said that he'd noticed me doing my homework every afternoon and that I must get good grades with all the time I spent on lessons. One thing led to another and he asked me if I'd like to go to a movie with him. Bishop, he was four years older than I was, but I don't think he knew I was in the eighth grade. I've always looked mature for my age."

She stopped talking and looked over my head. A huge sigh escaped her.

"This is where it really gets tough, Bishop." She reached for another tissue and sat there gathering her composure. Finally she began again. "I knew Daddy wouldn't let me go on a date, but I was so desperate to find someone, anyone, to be my friend. I told Ted—that was his name, Ted—that I'd go to a movie with him the next night. He asked me where I lived, and I told him I'd meet him at the theater. Our town only had one theater. He looked a little puzzled but agreed. All that night I tried to figure out how I was going to get out of the house to meet with Ted. I knew Daddy would demand to know where I was going. So the next night I told Mom and Daddy that I was going to a friend's house to study. Daddy was surprised, since I'd never done this before. 'Whose house?' he wanted to know. I just made up a name and said I was going to Janet's house and I hurried out the door before he could ask anything else.

"I walked the half-dozen blocks to the theater and got there just before Ted drove up in his Camaro. We saw the movie—funny, I can't remember what the title was, but I was pretty nervous. I was scared to have told Daddy a lie, and knew I'd pay for it if he found out, and I was nervous about my first date. When the movie was over we walked out of the theater, and Ted told me to get into his car. I told him I'd just walk home, but he insisted that he drive me. We drove around town for quite a while until I told Ted I needed to get home. I knew if I wasn't home before ten o'clock, Daddy would be angry—if he was home. Well, Ted pulled up in front of my house and I jumped right out and started up the walk before he could get out of the car. At that moment Daddy opened the front door just in time to see Ted's car pulling away. Daddy was pretty drunk. He staggered down the front steps and took a few steps down the sidewalk. 'Where have you been, girl?' he screamed, and grabbed me by the shoulders and started shaking and slapping me. Mom came out on the front porch and told Daddy to let me go. He acted as if he hadn't even heard her. Mom grabbed a broom from the corner of the porch and started beating Daddy on the back with the broomstick.

"Daddy let go of me and grabbed the broom. He hit Mom on the side of her head with the broomstick and then climbed into our old Ford pickup truck and took off. I helped Mom into the house and washed the blood out of her hair. Mom went to bed and I sat in the dark on the couch in our living room blaming myself for what had happened. I was still there an hour later when a police car pulled up in front of our house. We only had one policeman on duty each night; Jim Kirby was the one on duty that night. He climbed out of the car and walked up to our front door. Before he rang the bell, I turned on the porch light. He looked embarrassed. He said, 'Becky, is your mom home?'

"Bishop, we were so used to having Daddy brought home drunk by one of the local police that I wasn't even alarmed. I asked Jim to come into the house and then went into the bedroom and got Mom. She pulled her bathrobe around her and walked into the front room. 'Did you have to put him in jail, Jim?' she asked. 'No, ma'am,' he replied. 'There's never an easy way to say this. Your husband was driving pretty fast up on the mountain road. I think he'd been drinking. Anyway, he missed the curve near Ashby's farm and ran into a telephone pole.' He paused for a moment. 'He was dead when we got there.'"

Becky Butler stopped talking and looked at the carpet in front of her. I started to say something, but the Spirit whispered, *Be quiet, let her speak.*

Nearly a minute passed before she looked up and started to speak again. "So you see, Bishop, I caused my father's death. If I hadn't gone out with Ted, if I hadn't lied to Daddy about where I was going, he never would have started beating me and Mom wouldn't have hit him and he wouldn't have driven off, and . . . he'd still be alive today."

I cleared my throat. *There's more to hear,* whispered the Spirit.

Sister Butler crossed her arms as if she were hugging herself and rocked back and forth slightly in her chair. "After the funeral Mom kind of seemed confused. Granny came to live with us, and we just survived as best we could. I started spending more and more time with Ted. Mom didn't seem to care. That next spring he graduated from school. I'd turned fourteen and I was scared to death that Ted would go off to college and leave me. It turned out he went to work on his grandpa's ranch just outside of town. I decided I'd do anything to keep Ted."

Sister Butler paused and took a deep breath. She gazed at the ceiling and then began speaking again. "Just before my fifteenth birthday I discovered I was pregnant. I didn't know how to tell Mom and Granny, and I sure didn't know how to tell Ted. When I was nearly five months along I began to show, and one night Ted said, 'Are you pregnant?' I was really scared because I thought he'd just leave me, and I didn't know what to do. But I finally told him I was pregnant with his baby. I guess I shouldn't have worried about Ted, 'cause the first thing he said was, 'Well, we'd better get married.'"

Sister Butler stood up from her chair and paced around the office. "Of course, I'd never gone to church, but Ted was sure his minister would marry us. Well, he was wrong. We finally drove to Nevada and got married. Mom and Granny weren't there, Ted's folks weren't there, it was just the two of us. Ted's grandpa had a guest house on his ranch, and he let us live there. Four months later little Teddy was born.

"Ted had a lot of stress on him. He worked long hours for his grandpa and there was never enough money to go around. One night Teddy woke up and started to cry. Ted got up and started shouting at him. He threatened to hit the baby if he didn't shut up. I went to Teddy's crib and started to pick him up to comfort him, but Ted pushed me out of the way and kept screaming at the baby. I tried again to pick him up, but Ted shoved me onto the bed and told me to stay there. Bishop, if it hadn't been so frightening it would have been ridiculous. Here was a nineteen-year-old man trying to bully a four-month-old baby into being quiet. At last Teddy cried himself to sleep, and Ted stomped out of the house. Things went from bad to worse after that. Ted was jealous of the time I spent with the baby. He started hitting me whenever he felt I wasn't doing what he wanted. He started staying out at night. Our marriage was going downhill fast."

Becky Butler stopped her pacing and sat back down in her chair. "Ted came in late one night and found me sitting up nursing Teddy. 'Becky,' he said, 'this just isn't working out. I never really loved you. I just married you because you were pregnant, and now I feel like I'm on a sinking ship. I really think we need to think about a divorce.'" She gave another sigh. "Well, we went to the courthouse and filed for divorce. I went back to live with Mom and Granny. I was barely sixteen years old, divorced, and with a baby. On top of that I'd dropped out of school and I didn't have any skills to help me find a job. So, Bishop, I not only caused my father's death, but

I'd had an immoral relationship and pretty well fouled up my life, Ted's life, and the baby's life."

She stopped talking and looked past me at the painting of the Savior. I cleared my throat again. *She isn't finished,* whispered the Spirit. *Just listen.*

"So there we were—Granny, Mom, and me, all living together. I got a job as a waitress at the truck stop on the edge of town. Granny and Mom were on welfare. They weren't too happy about taking care of Teddy while I worked, but reluctantly shared the task.

"One morning I was giving the baby a bath, when a knock came at the door. Granny answered it and then called out to Mom and me, 'Either of you two want to hear about religion?' Neither of us answered. 'Didn't think so,' said Granny. I walked out of the bathroom carrying Teddy wrapped in a towel and saw two young men dressed in blue suits standing outside the screen door. 'Ask them in, Granny,' I said.

"That was three years ago, Bishop. I will be thankful forever for those two wonderful young men who taught me about the love of the Savior and his atoning sacrifice for our sins. I was baptized six months later, much to the dismay of Mom and Granny. I completed my high school equivalency and I've learned secretarial skills. But as long as I was living with Mom it was as if I was living under the cloud of the past, and it was clear that she and Granny didn't want me there. Last month I was praying and I felt impressed to drive up to Salt Lake and try to find a place to live. I really didn't know where to look, so I just drove around looking for vacancy signs. Mrs. Walker had her basement apartment available, and it just seemed right. I've gotten a job and moved into your ward. But, Bishop, I'll understand if you don't want to welcome someone like me into your midst."

There was a knock on the door. "Excuse me, please,"

I said. When I opened the door, my ward clerk was standing there. "I've finished the work on the membership records," he told me. "Do you need me to stay?"

"If you would for just a few minutes. We're nearly finished, I think."

"I'll just sit here in the foyer," he said.

I returned to my desk. "Sister Butler, I want to make three points if I may. First, you were not responsible for your father's death. As much as we all like to place the blame on someone else, by the time we've reached adulthood we are responsible for our own actions. This is not a new problem—trying to shift the blame. When the Lord asked Adam if he had eaten the forbidden fruit, instead of giving the simple answer 'Yes' Adam shifted the blame to Eve. She shifted it to the serpent. Your father made the decision to get in his car; you didn't make it for him. Nor is there anything you can do to bring him back. It appears to me you and your mother absorbed years of abuse from your father. No one deserves that kind of treatment. What you must do is learn to forgive him. But, I repeat, you were not responsible for your father's death.

"The second point I'd like to make is that the Savior does indeed love you. He paid the ultimate sacrifice for you and for me. Through his unspeakable agony in Gethsemane and on the cross, he provided for us a way to repent and have our sins forgiven. We have often been counseled to hate the sin but love the sinner. Unless I am mistaken, you had gone through a period of repentance prior to your baptism, and when you were buried in the water and brought forth it was indeed a rebirth and your sins were washed away. However, I am fairly certain there is one person who has not forgiven you of this sin in your life—you. So, I would tell you that not only do you need to learn to forgive your father, you need to learn to forgive yourself, difficult though you may find that to be.

"And finally, the third point is that not only do we welcome you into this ward, we are overjoyed to have you in our ward. And anytime you need to talk further, I'm available."

Tears ran down her cheeks, but she smiled through them and said, "Thank you, Bishop. Can I ask one other thing from you? I know it's getting late. Teddy's probably giving the baby-sitter fits, but I've never had the pleasure of having the priesthood in my home. Would you give me a blessing before I go?"

I stepped from behind my desk and stood behind Becky Butler. After placing my hands on her head, I began to give her a blessing. As the blessing proceeded I heard myself say, "I promise you that there is a worthy young man waiting for you who will be your companion not only for this life but for eternity." I completed the blessing, and Sister Butler and I walked to the door. She shook my hand as I let her out. "See you Sunday," I said.

"Yes, you will . . . yes, you will." She walked out into the snow-covered parking lot.

"Let's go home, Brother Dave," I said to my ward clerk. "I appreciate your staying so late."

"No problem, Bishop. Did you get the information so I can send for her membership?"

"I forgot to ask," I said. "I'll have it for you Sunday."

❤

Sunday came, and Sister Butler and Teddy sat on the front row again, all alone. At the end of sacrament meeting she didn't leave as she had the week before. My wife came up and introduced herself, and the following week Teddy and his mother were sitting in front of my wife and children. Two weeks later her membership records arrived and she was formally welcomed into the ward. Shortly thereafter she was called to teach a class of four-year-olds in Primary.

Winter melted into spring. Our chapel was close enough that I could walk from home to the church. As I was passing the Farnsworth's home, I noticed Randall Farnsworth's car in the driveway. Randall's car was hard to miss—it was a twenty-year-old Dodge with nearly equal amounts of rust and metal. Although the car once was a dark green, now the hood was white and the trunk was tan. Randall was the oldest of nine children and had been attending college in Oregon. As I walked by I tried to remember whether he had finished three or four years of college. I thought back to when he was a twelve-year-old deacon and I had found him stacking all of the chairs in his basement classroom on top of each other and then climbing up them and out the window.

My next run-in with him was when I found him in the church at midnight playing basketball. He'd stuck pebbles in the outside doors to keep them from closing all the way, and he and a half-dozen of his friends were having a friendly game of hoops. Despite our confrontations, I still considered us good friends. He'd gone on a mission to California, and after returning he'd gone to Oregon to go to school.

The Farnsworths' door flew open and Randall came crashing out. "Bishop, how the heck are you? Gee, it's good to see you." He threw his arms around me.

"It's great to see you too, Randall. I was just trying to figure out if you were through with school."

"Bishop, you are looking at a college graduate." He spread out his arms and turned around. "Do I look any different?"

"Nope, just as crazy as ever. Congratulations! What now?"

"I have two job interviews in the morning. Both of them look pretty promising. I'm just excited to be home. You're probably on your way to church. Sorry if I held you up. See you in sacrament meeting." He spun around and waved as he rushed back into the house.

❤

As I stood to conduct sacrament meeting, I noticed that quite a number of our young people were back from college. I welcomed them home. The meeting progressed as we had planned it. Finally I stood to announce the closing hymn and prayer. "We'd like to thank all those who participated in our sacrament service today. We will now sing the closing hymn, number 153, 'Lord, We Ask Thee Ere We Part,' and the benediction will be offered by Sister Becky Butler."

After the hymn had been sung, Sister Butler made her way to the pulpit to offer the closing prayer. She offered a sweet, sincere prayer. As she finished, I stood to shake her hand and saw Randall Farnsworth hurrying down the aisle. He jumped the three steps to the stand in a single bound and spun Sister Butler around. He enveloped her in a bear hug.

"Elder Farnsworth," she stammered, "what are you doing here?"

"My question exactly," he said. "What are you doing in Utah?"

"Excuse me," I interjected. "Do you two know each other?"

"Oh, Bishop," said Becky Butler, "Elder Farnsworth is the missionary who baptized me. He baptized me and then he was transferred."

"I baptized her, then I came home, is more like it." He turned to Becky. "Where's Teddy? He was the cutest little kid." Becky led him off the stand to where Teddy was sitting next to my wife. Randall picked him up, held him at arm's length, and admired him.

❤

During Sunday dinner my wife asked, "Where in the world did Randall know Becky from? They sure seemed like old friends."

"He was the elder who baptized her," I replied.

"They make a handsome couple," my wife said. "She's such a pretty girl, and he's really turned out to be quite a good-looking man."

❤

Spring blossomed into summer, and summer ripened into autumn. My wife and I were taking a walk through the ward admiring the scarlet and gold flame of leaves, when we heard someone call to us. "Bishop, wait up." It was Randall Farnsworth.

"Hi, Randall, what's up?"

"Bishop, I need to talk to you. You know Becky and I have been dating for quite some time, and—well, there are some things from the past I need to ask you about. Is there some time we can get together soon?"

"What if I walk home and get the keys to the church. I'll meet you there in half an hour if that's okay."

"Thanks, Bishop," he said quietly.

My wife and I started home. "You're awfully quiet," she said after a few minutes. "Is something wrong?"

"I hope not," I replied.

A few minutes later Randall and I sat in my office. "Bishop, I appreciate your meeting with me on such short notice," he said.

"No problem, Randall."

"I guess I might as well plunge right in. You know Becky and I have been seeing quite a bit of each other." He looked at me for confirmation. I nodded my head. "Well, it has reached a point where I'm really considering asking her to marry me."

I nodded my head, leaned back in my chair, and put my fingertips together.

"I'm making good money. I've even bought a new car, but Bishop, there's something that's really bothering me." He looked down. "I guess it shouldn't—I mean, I know about repentance, but . . . ." He paused.

I cleared my throat. *Just listen,* whispered the Spirit.

"Bishop, you know what a little hellion I was growing up in this ward."

I smiled and nodded my head.

"I don't know whether I'm good enough for Becky. I've never told her about all those mean little tricks I played as a boy, and I don't know whether she'll forgive me."

I smiled. "Randall, she will; believe me, she will."

Four months later Becky Butler became Becky Farnsworth as the two of them were married in the Salt Lake Temple. They came home from their honeymoon to an apartment outside our ward boundaries. We had to find another Primary teacher, but it was worth it.

CHAPTER 9

♥

Communication is a wonderful thing. Lack of communication is probably one of the most common of all problems in marriages.

$\mathcal{T}$he first year I was serving as a bishop, the executive secretary of our ward was very efficient at contacting people to remind them when their temple recommends expired. Most people appreciated the reminder and promptly made an appointment for an interview.

One Sunday he placed a list of appointments in front of me. I looked at the names. At two o'clock Brother James Nesmith was due for a temple recommend interview. "What about Sister Nesmith?"

"I don't know. Actually, she was the one I talked to, and she said her husband would be happy to visit with you. Maybe she'll come too." But she didn't.

Temple recommends expire quarterly, and although married couples are encouraged to hold recommends that expire the same quarter, it is not uncommon for husbands and wives to have different expiration dates. So I was not too concerned when Fiona Nesmith did not appear with her husband.

Sister Nesmith did not appear the following quarter, nor the one after that, nor the one after that. A year passed and her husband appeared in my office for another interview.

"What about your wife, Brother Nesmith?" I asked. "Doesn't she need a recommend interview, too?"

One white eyebrow raised a little. "You'll have to ask her about that, Bishop," was all he said. I noticed that his shoulders drooped a little as he walked out of my office.

I scratched my head. James and Fiona Nesmith were two solid pillars of the ward. Both now in their seventies, they had lived for nearly fifty years in the same house they'd purchased a year into their marriage. Salt-of-the-earth people, those who knew them were quick to say.

James stood ramrod straight and spare, an inch over six feet tall. His full mane of silver hair was always neatly parted just above his left ear and carefully combed. He sported a pencil-thin silver mustache on his upper lip and a pair of gold-rimmed eyeglasses that were perched upon his aquiline nose. He looked every inch a country gentleman.

Fiona was just as thin and ramrod straight as her husband, although she was a full foot shorter than he. Her hair was so meticulously cared for that it appeared she attended the beauty shop every morning.

The two of them had owned and operated a small corner grocery store until it was consumed by a strip mall five years before. Generous to a fault, they were the epitome of Christian living.

I picked up the phone and called their number. "Hello," warbled Fiona Nesmith.

"Sister Nesmith, this is the bishop. I wonder if you have time for a temple recommend interview this afternoon?"

"I'm sorry, Bishop," she replied. "I don't think this afternoon will work out at all. Thank you for calling. Good-bye." She hung up before I could get another word in. I wondered what was going on.

I picked up the phone again and dialed the previous bishop. When he answered, I said, "Tell me what you know about Fiona Nesmith. I just tried to set up a temple recommend interview and she turned me down flat. Did you have any trouble getting her in for an interview?"

"Never saw her," said the previous bishop. "We tried to set up appointments several times, but she always refused. I always thought it was strange. James came in regular as clockwork. He goes to the temple a couple of times a week now that he's retired, but I could never get Fiona in for an interview. Good luck."

"Thanks. We'll keep trying." I leaned back in my chair and pondered what I knew about the Nesmiths. The previous year they had celebrated their fiftieth wedding anniversary. All eight of their children were there, as I remembered. Four boys and four girls. All of them were married, and all had children who attended. I hadn't quite been able to put together who was married to whom and which children belonged to which couple, but it had been a fairly good crowd. They seemed to be a close-knit family.

I wrote the Nesmiths down on my "to-do" list. It was a busy time of year, and nearly three weeks passed before I was driving past the Nesmiths' home and decided to drop in for a visit. Brother Nesmith saw me as I walked across the lawn, and opened the front door before I arrived. "Come in, Bishop. Always good to have you visit." I shook his hand and entered the cool comfort of their living room.

Sister Nesmith was dusting flour from her hands as she walked into the room from her kitchen. "Bishop, so nice to have you call," she said. "Please, please have a seat." She pointed to a rocking chair on one side of the fireplace.

The mantel above the fireplace was covered with framed pictures of what seemed to be dozens of children. I stopped and admired the collection. "Quite a family you have here. How many are there now?"

"Eight children," said Fiona quickly, "thirty-nine grand-children, and four great-grandchildren, and two on the way. Makes quite a group when we get together for a family reunion."

"I'd guess they're spread all over the place," I said.

"No, no," replied Fiona. "All of them live within an hour's drive of here. Jim—that's James Junior—and Tamara live in Farmington. He's a counselor in the bish-opric in their ward. Franklin and Anita live in Woods Cross; she's the Relief Society president and he's on the stake high council." On and on she went, telling me about each of their children and their activities in the Church.

"The two of you have been married over fifty years," I said. "That's quite an accomplishment in and of itself."

"Oh, Bishop, it's not hard at all when you have a good woman like Fiona," smiled James as he patted his wife's hand. She beamed a radiant smile in his direction. He reached over and brushed a dusting of flour from her cheek. "You know, Bishop, I can honestly say my wife has never disappointed me in all the years I've known her. She is my best friend and confidante. She is the best thing that ever happened to me."

"Oh, James," she said demurely, "you're so full of blarney."

The small talk continued for a few minutes in this room so obviously filled with love. Then I asked, "Sister Fiona, I believe your temple recommend has expired. We need to have an interview."

She looked straight at me and said, "Oh, not today, Bishop, I've got too much to get done. Maybe next week." James's jaw hardened slightly.

"What time next Sunday would be convenient for you?" I pressed.

"Well now, let's see," she mumbled. "You know Sunday is going to be a pretty busy day. Some of our children are coming to visit. Perhaps we'll have to postpone that until the next week."

"Sister Fiona," I said quietly, "it is not my intent to badger anyone into an interview, but I think you are purposefully avoiding me. Whenever you're ready, please let me know. I love the two of you too much to just let this drop. I hope you believe that."

"I know, Bishop, I know," she said, almost in a whisper.

James cleared his throat and stood up. Clearly the visit was over. "Thank you for visiting us. You're welcome anytime." He opened the door for me. I shook Sister Nesmith's hand and noticed that her eyes were wet. I shook James's hand and left. I could not for the life of me understand what could be out of place in Fiona Nesmith's life.

❤

At our Sunday services we honored a young man who had just returned from a two-year mission in Argentina. He was a popular young man, with a large family and many friends. The crowd was enormous. I noticed the Nesmiths enter a few minutes late and sit on folding chairs in the overflow area behind the chapel. Following the administration of the sacrament the young returned missionary spoke eloquently about his experiences in the mission field. He spoke of humble people who hungered and thirsted for the gospel of Jesus Christ.

"Their baptisms were truly a rebirth," he proclaimed. "They were washed clean of their past sins and stood there as innocent as newborn children. Today, when we partook of the sacrament, we renewed our baptismal covenant. Brothers and sisters, think what a blessing it is to have our sins remitted through the atoning sacrifice of the Savior, if we but repent and strive to follow his commandments. 'If ye love me, keep my commandments,' was all he asked."

I thought back two years to the sacrament meeting where we honored an immature, somewhat rowdy teenager, who now stood before us as a self-assured, mature young man. The change was amazing.

The meeting ended and a congratulatory throng surrounded the missionary and his family in the foyer outside my office. It took nearly half an hour for the crowd to disperse. I heard a timid knock on my office door.

"Sister Nesmith," I exclaimed as I opened the door. "Please come in."

"Thank you, Bishop. I need to make an appointment for an interview."

I glanced at the list of appointments on my calendar. The executive secretary had left me an hour to go home and eat before interviews began. "Why not right now?" I indicated a chair in front of the desk and closed the door.

"Are you sure, Bishop? I thought perhaps I could get on your calendar for next week." I heard the quavering note in her voice.

"Now would be just fine, Sister Fiona. Please have a seat." She perched on the edge of the chair like a bird ready to take flight. "Is this a temple recommend interview?" I asked. "Or do we just need to talk?"

Tears began to roll down her weathered cheeks. "Oh, Bishop, I'm so ashamed," she blurted out. She began to sob.

I handed her a box of tissues. "Take your time," I said softly.

She nodded her head. "Bishop, I'm a thief." Her whole frame shook as she convulsed into sobs. "I'm a thief," she gulped, one word at a time. Leaning forward, she placed her hands flat on my desk, laid her forehead on the backs of her hands, and wept.

"Would you like to tell me about it?" I asked, almost in a whisper.

She lifted her head. "No, I wouldn't *like* to . . . but I must. I've avoided you too long." The sobs continued. "Oh, Bishop, how could I have been so stupid?" She covered her face with her hands.

I waited.

"How could I have done this to someone I love so much?" At length she was able to control her sobbing. She wiped her face with the tissue and took another from the box. "For so long I've tried to justify what I did. But it was wrong. It was wrong." Her clear blue eyes shone as she looked at me. "I worked for James before we were married, did you know that?"

I shook my head. "That must have been quite a long time ago."

She nodded. "It was during the Depression. My father lost his job. My mother was taking in laundry. We were in desperate straits, Bishop. James hired me to work in his grocery store. His father owned it, really, but his health was poor, and James pretty well took care of the place himself. He hired me to stock shelves and fill orders. Many of our customers kept their families alive on credit. After a while James taught me how to keep the books. He was such a good, generous man."

Her voice trailed off as her mind returned to what appeared to be treasured memories. "Then my sister announced her engagement. I don't know if you've ever met my older sister, Bishop; she visits with us every once in a while. Her husband died nearly fifteen years ago. She's getting harder to take care of. We may have to put her in a nursing home."

"Those can be tough decisions," I said. I sensed Fiona was stalling for time.

Sister Nesmith swallowed hard. "That's when it happened, Bishop. That's when I became a thief." She began to sob again. It took a few minutes until her crying subsided enough for her to continue. "We so desperately wanted to have a nice wedding for Clara—that's my sister—but we had so little money. Mother wanted to bake Clara a wedding cake, but every bit of flour we had was used to bake bread for the family. I knew how very, very much Mother wanted to bake that cake. At the end of the day I often began filling orders that customers were going to pick up the next morning. James was sweeping the floor, and I just—just sort of filled an extra order. I put all of the ingredients Mother needed to bake a cake into a box. Then I said good night to James and carried that box out the door. Clara had her cake and I became a thief."

"When did you say this was, Sister Nesmith?"

"March fourteenth, 1932," she said without a pause.

"Is there more to the story?" I asked.

"The wedding cake was beautiful. James was invited to the open house, and he admired the cake. Of course, that's when he first asked me if he could see me socially. We began seeing each other quite often. A year later we were married. This wonderful, generous, honest man married a thief."

"May I ask you a question, Sister Fiona?" She nodded her head. "How much do you think the groceries were worth?"

"One dollar and thirteen cents," she said immediately. "Oh, Bishop, I paid for the groceries out of my next paycheck. I kept the books. I held back one dollar and thirteen cents from what was owed me. But, Bishop, that doesn't excuse my thievery."

"Is there anything else you need to confess to me?" I asked. She shook her head. I looked at this good, good woman who still sat perched on the edge of her chair. "You are telling me that because of one minor event in your life, which you obviously paid back, that you have not had a temple recommend for fifty years?" She nodded her head again. "You missed seeing each of your eight children married in the temple because of one dollar and thirteen cents?"

She placed her hands back on the edge of the desk and shook her head. The tears began again. "Oh, how I wanted to be there," she sobbed. "James was there. James was always there for the children."

"Sister Fiona, don't you believe in repentance?"

"Bishop, I've never been able to bring myself to confess to anyone before."

"Have you ever told James?"

The sobs erupted again. "Of course not. He'd never understand. He's never been a thief."

"Sister Nesmith, haven't you been in Gethsemane long enough?" She looked at me quizzically. "I'm going to call your husband and ask him to come over here," I said.

A look of fear came into her eyes. "Oh, no, Bishop. I can't face him. He'll never forgive me."

"Fiona, don't you know him better than that after all these years?" I picked up the phone and dialed their number. James answered. "Brother James, this is the bishop. I have your lovely bride in my office, and I wonder if you could join us."

"I'll be right there, Bishop." And within five minutes we heard a knock on the door.

James Nesmith entered my office and pulled a chair up next to his wife. He put his arm lovingly around her shoulders.

"Brother James, your wife has just explained to me why she has never held a temple recommend," I told him. Sister Nesmith's sobbing began anew.

"You mean because of the wedding cake?" he said softly. Fiona's head jerked back and she stared at her husband.

"You knew?" she blurted out. "How?"

"You kept the books, of course, but I always checked

over them. When I saw you'd shorted yourself, I put two and two together. After all, at Clara's wedding your mother thanked me for providing the ingredients for the cake." His eyes misted. "I've always felt bad about that, you know. I knew Clara was getting married, and I knew your family was struggling. I've never forgiven myself for not contributing more freely to the open house."

"More freely?" I questioned.

"Well, I'd already given Fiona's mother the cold cuts and the potatoes for the potato salad. I was trying to get in good with her so she'd let me court her beautiful daughter." He squeezed his wife's shoulders. "I don't know why I didn't think of the cake. I've always blamed myself for that."

"Brother Nesmith, would you step out in the hall while I interview your wife for her temple recommend?"

He smiled broadly. "Nothing would make me happier, Bishop."

CHAPTER 10

❤

Whatever may befall thee,
it was preordained for thee
from everlasting.
—Marcus Aurelius Antoninus

I've heard people say their marriage was made in heaven—that they were predestined to meet and marry. Others have suggested that there was only one person who was meant for them, and they've spent their lives looking for that particular soul. I've been skeptical, to say the least. One of my dear friends assures me that he was never attracted to any girl until he met his wife. I've noticed she always changes the subject at that point, but then she knows I knew her in her teen years and remember the trail of broken hearts she left behind. My background in science leads me to believe that there are explanations for most of the events we count as coincidence, but I must admit that our son, Stan, and his wife, Brenda, have a story that's a little hard to write off as pure coincidence.

The story begins long before I met my beautiful wife, Janice. When Stan was fourteen years old they were living in Twin Falls, Idaho, a three-and-a-half-hour drive from Salt Lake City. Many members of the family lived in Salt Lake, and occasionally Janice and her boys made excursions there.

"Mom, next time we go to Salt Lake can Rick and I go to Lagoon?" Stan asked one day. Rick was Stan's friend who lived next door. Lagoon is an amusement park about twenty miles north of Salt Lake City.

"We'll see, Stan."

"Please, Mom, please."

"We'll see, Stan."

For the next three weeks Stan planted hints, asked when they were going, and generally made a nuisance of himself. At last a trip to Salt Lake was planned, and Rick was invited. They left Twin Falls fairly early in the morning and arrived at Lagoon just as it was opening for the day.

"Stan, how much money did you bring with you?" asked his mother.

"Enough, Mom, enough," replied Stan.

"You two remember that we'll be here at eight-thirty to pick you up."

"We'll be here. No problem."

"Stan, did you remember to wear your watch?"

"Yes, Mom."

"Eight-thirty. Here by the gate, boys."

"Yes, Mom."

"We want to be home by midnight. Now, you boys behave yourselves."

"We will, Mom."

Janice drove off toward Salt Lake City, leaving the two of them standing by the front gate of Lagoon. Stan and Rick waved good-bye, checked the money in their pockets, and hurried into Lagoon. The midway rides didn't open for two hours, but there was another attraction they were eager to visit.

Lagoon boasted a million-gallon swimming pool with "water fit to drink." Both Stan and Rick were accomplished swimmers. The swimming pool had both low and high diving boards. Stan and Rick cannon-balled off the low board with all the abandon of youth. The water splashed high in the air and splattered down on people who were suntanning themselves on the grass at the edge of the pool. Two girls lying in the sun at the side of the pool complained loudly that they were getting wet. Stan smiled at Rick. Rick smiled at Stan. They moved from the low board to the high board in order to generate a bigger splash. This time when the water splashed on the girls, they squealed. Stan swam to the edge of the pool near the girls and splashed water on their oiled skins. Quickly he swam underwater out of the diving area. When he surfaced, one of the girls was ready with a pail full of water to pour on his head. A water fight erupted, and by the time it ended the four fourteen-year-olds had decided to spend the day together.

"What's your name?" Stan asked his new companion as she emerged from the swimming pool dressing room.

"Brenda. What's yours?"

As Stan was introducing himself, the midway opened. "Let's head to the roller coaster," he called to Rick. He grabbed Brenda's hand and pulled her toward the coaster.

Stan and Brenda sat in the front seat as it screamed around its course. They challenged each other to let go of the handle and keep both hands in the air. Then they rode in the backseat to compare the ride. They spun around on the Tilt-A-Whirl, hung upside down in the Roll-A-Plane, and ate snow cones and cotton candy.

"Want to go on the Terror Ride?" Stan asked.

"Sure," replied Brenda. They stood in line, climbed into the car, and rode into the darkened tunnel. Cauldrons bubbled, skeletons danced, and Stan protectively slipped his arm around Brenda's shoulders. The day was turning out even better than they had hoped.

They entered the Penny Arcade and had their pictures taken in the four-for-a-dollar picture booth. Stan carefully punched out "Stan and Brenda Forever" on an aluminum key chain fob, which he presented to Brenda. They played the pinball machines and tried to grab a prize with the Erie digger.

The two couples walked hand in hand through the park. Stan and Rick rolled balls up the Ski-Ball and won tickets to be exchanged for prizes. Suddenly, Stan checked his watch. It was nearly eight-thirty.

Stan picked up a sheet of paper advertising a coming event and wrote his name and address. He ripped the paper in half and wrote Brenda's. The couples said good-bye and parted. Brenda and her friend went home to Centerville, five miles south of Lagoon. Stan and Rick waited outside the gate for about five minutes until Janice arrived.

"Have a good time?"

"It was okay," said Stan.

"How was swimming?"

Stan shrugged his shoulders. "Okay, I guess."

"Did you get to ride all the rides?"

"Yup," said Stan as he leaned back against the seat and closed his eyes.

The next morning Brenda smoothed out the piece of paper with Stan's address. She wrote him a short note thanking him for the fun time at Lagoon. She enclosed a junior high school yearbook picture and mailed it off to Twin Falls. She put the aluminum key chain fob in her dresser drawer.

When the letter arrived, Stan read it and put the picture in the sock drawer in his dresser. He didn't write back. Brenda didn't write a second letter. Theirs was a one-day summer romance. Apparently.

Four years later Stan graduated from high school. The commitments in Twin Falls were over, and Janice, Stan, and his younger brother, Brett, moved to Bountiful, a community between Centerville and Salt Lake City. Stan and Brenda were now living less than five miles apart. That summer Stan applied for admission to Utah State University in Logan. Before he left Bountiful for Logan, he often drove through Centerville—not, however, in search of Brenda. He'd long since forgotten her address, and he and Brenda never bumped into each other. Obviously the romance was over.

After two years at Utah State University, Stan decided to go on a mission for The Church of Jesus Christ of Latter-day Saints. He talked with his bishop, filled out his papers, and waited. After a couple of weeks, the call came for him to serve in the Ireland Dublin Mission. Brenda did not notice the announcement of his missionary farewell in the local newspaper and, of course, did not attend it. Stan left for Ireland to serve his mission. Although a number of girls wrote letters to him while he was away, Brenda was not one of them. Their paths had parted and they seemed destined to never cross again.

About a month before Stan was to be released, Janice and I married. We moved furniture across Bountiful from her home to mine. One of the slightly uncomfortable facts in our relationship was that Stan had never met me, and I had a son, Derick, serving a mission in Los Angeles, who had never met Janice. Stan would be coming to a home that was different from the one he'd left, and to six new stepbrothers and stepsisters. Derick would be returning to two new stepbrothers.

In order to soften the blow to some extent, Janice and I traveled to Ireland at the end of Stan's mission to pick him up and give him a chance to meet me. For a week we toured Ireland and England together. We arrived home in October, and Stan prepared to reenroll at Utah State in January. During the next three months, while he was living in Bountiful, Stan didn't ever see Brenda. In fact, Stan had apparently forgotten Brenda. The romance was ended.

In the time since their summer romance at Lagoon, Brenda finished junior high school in Centerville and attended and graduated from Viewmont High School. She had an intense interest and talent in interior design and decided to attend college and major in that field. She enrolled at Utah State University. In fact, the year before Stan's mission the two of them were both in Logan attending Utah State University, but with Stan majoring in political science and Brenda in interior design, their paths never crossed.

Stan drove to Logan to find somewhere to live—not an easy task in a small college town. No campus housing was available and there were few advertisements in the local paper, but after considerable searching he located three other returned missionaries who had rented an off-campus apartment that was large enough for four people. They were glad to have Stan share expenses. The next Saturday Stan loaded up his bed and dresser and the other necessities of life into our van and drove to Logan to get moved in.

His dresser was fairly bulky, and in order to move it more easily, he removed the drawers. One of his roommates was helping him move the dresser, and as he replaced the bottom drawer he spotted a picture that had fallen to the bottom of the dresser. He retrieved it.

"Is this your little sister?" he asked Stan as he handed him Brenda's picture.

Stan studied the picture for some time, trying to remember who it was. "Just a girl I met a long time ago," he said finally. He put it on top of his dresser. He left Logan and drove the van back to Bountiful. The next day after church, he drove back to Logan and spent the first night in his new apartment.

Early the next morning he walked out of the door in time to make it to his first class. Two apartments faced each other across the stairwell. Just as Stan walked out, the door of the other apartment opened and a girl walked out. They looked at each other. The girl's eyes widened and she said, "Isn't your name Stan?"

Coincidence? Fate? Who knows. But after an eight-year hiatus, love blossomed again. After all, who can argue with destiny? Later that year they were married, and they moved into their own apartment in Logan. A few weeks later they were visiting Brenda's family, and her niece wandered into the room dragging her teddy bear. Around its neck was a necklace with an aluminum fob that said, "Stan and Brenda Forever."

We hope so.

CHAPTER 11

♥

Sometimes love spawns bravery.

*M*y brothers all were great basketball players. My wife was a great basketball player. I am a great basketball fan. We were excited when professional basketball came to Salt Lake City. One Saturday afternoon my wife and I had the opportunity to attend a game in the Salt Palace. The team we were playing did not have a spectacular record. It was an afternoon game. The game was being played the day before Scout Sunday. Perhaps for any or all of these reasons, the promotional office had elected to let anyone in a Scout uniform attend the game for a one-dollar admission fee.

We were lucky enough to have aisle seats, although they were up fairly high. Just as we sat down a pack of Cub Scouts arrived. They had the next eleven seats. Ten Cubs and their den mother. We stood up and let the Cubs decide who was sitting next to whom. They finally filed into their seats and we sat back down.

The Cub Scout sitting next to me was dressed in his blue and gold uniform, complete with neckerchief and cap. Nothing was out of place. He was the consummate Cub Scout. I read the pack number from his shoulder patches.

"Where are you from?" I ventured.

A pair of black, almond-shaped eyes stared into my face. "Magna, Utah," he said with a trace of an accent. A huge grin split his face, revealing a row of perfectly spaced, gleaming white teeth. He jumped to his feet and extended his hand. I shook it. "May I be so bold," he said, "as to ask where you are from?"

I forced myself to keep from smiling too broadly as I told him where we were from.

"My name," he continued, "is Jian Li Parker." I told him my name. He sat back down and adjusted his neckerchief. "We are very fortunate to be able to come to this basketball game, I think," he mused. The Cub on Jian Li's other side poked him on the arm. The two of them engaged in a conversation that included several giggles.

People continued to file into the Salt Palace. I glanced at my watch. The game was scheduled to start in fifteen minutes. I felt a gentle pull on my sleeve. I turned and looked into those beautiful eyes. "This is a wondrous sight, is it not?" He was perched on the edge of his seat looking at the throngs of people parading in. The two basketball teams were warming up on the floor of the arena.

"Where were you born, Jian Li?" I asked.

"Vietnam," he responded. "But I left there nearly three years ago." A dark cloud seemed to cover his face. "It was not a pleasant place; there is much suffering there." After a brief pause he smiled his gleaming smile at me.

"How old are you now?"

"I am eight years old. I am a Wolf Scout." He proudly showed me the wolf head neckerchief slide he wore.

I didn't want to pry, but I was curious to know more about this little Cub Scout. "How did you come to the United States?"

"By airplane," he teased. Then, through his infectious grin, he said, "I was adopted. That is my mother." He pointed at the den mother who was seated at the other end of the line of Cub Scouts. Jian Li waved at her, and a radiant smile covered her face as she waved back. She was an ample woman about forty years of age.

"Do you have any brothers and sisters?" I asked.

"Not yet," he smiled. "As of this moment, I am an only child." He sighed and shook his head, then looked at me and said, "But I don't mind." His smile reappeared.

I saw Jian Li's gaze wander down the steps that led to our seats. A man about twenty-five years of age was making his way up them. His hair hung down past the shoulders of his sleeveless denim jacket. A red baseball cap was jammed down over his hair. The bill of the cap was almost black from grease stains. Although the arena was fairly dark, he wore a pair of aviator sunglasses. He had an unkempt full beard and mustache that hung down nearly to the middle of his chest, partially obscuring the peace sign that was crudely drawn on his tee-shirt. The knees of his Levi's were practically nonexistent, and the tops of his engineer boots were adorned with pieces of chain. He climbed the stairs until he reached the row of seats directly in front of us, and, spying the empty seat on the aisle, he dropped heavily into it. We were assailed by the odor of alcohol and tobacco. Jian Li wrinkled his nose.

The teams finished their warm-up routines and left the floor. The announcer welcomed us to the Salt Palace. He began a litany of future events, promotions, and regulations about the arena.

"Is this your first time at the Salt Palace?" I asked.

"Yes. It is quite an enjoyable event, is it not?" he replied.

I smiled at his use of English. He had practically lost his accent, but his sentence structure was quite stilted. He was still on the edge of his seat, and his eyes took in everything that was happening.

The teams returned and huddled together on either side of the scorekeeper's table. The announcer called out the names of the members of the visiting team. Each man waved to the unappreciative crowd as his name was called. As the starting five were announced, they jogged to the center of the court and gave each other high fives. There was a small smattering of applause and a few boos from the crowd.

The arena was darkened. The announcer announced our home team. A spotlight picked out each player as his name was called. The crowd erupted in applause. The starting five took their places in the center of the court. Applause, whistles, and cheers exploded from the crowd. The players gave each other a collective high five.

At the far end of the court, the spotlight picked up the Stars and Stripes as it hung from the rafters. "Will the audience please rise for the national anthem," the announcer intoned.

Jian Li Parker hopped from his seat and snapped to attention. He folded the ring finger and little finger of his hand and extended the other two fingers just under the bill of his cap. I arose and placed my hand over my heart.

An amplified introduction to the anthem boomed from the speakers high above the floor of the arena. I focused my attention on the flag. Someone tapped me on my leg. "Excuse me," said Jian Li. Still holding his salute, he sidled past my wife and me to the aisle. He stepped gingerly down the steps until he was beside the unkempt figure in the seat in front of my wife. He had not risen. He was still sprawled in his seat.

Jian Li looked him straight in the eye. "Stand up, mister," he commanded. "And take off your hat. It's our country. Show some respect."

"Oh say, can you see . . ."

Slowly the man rose from his seat. He reached up and took off his hat.

"Put it over your heart, mister," Jian Li whispered loudly.

The man complied.

Jian Li continued his salute until the anthem ended. He returned to his seat. I reached over and patted his hand.

"Some people don't know how lucky they are," was all he said.

CHAPTER 12

❤

With no apparent beauty,
that man should him desire . . .
—William W. Phelps

One late afternoon I sat at my computer working on a presentation that I was to give the following week, when I heard a key in the lock of my office door. The door opened and our custodian stuck his head into the room. "I'm sorry," he said, "I didn't know you were still here. I'll come back later."

"No, no, Walter, come on in. It's time for me to quit for the night anyway."

"Are you sure? I can come back later. It'll be no problem."

I assured him I was just leaving. As I retrieved my suit coat from the hanger on the back of the door, Walter entered my office dragging his portable garbage bin behind him. He quickly emptied my wastebasket and then began dusting the surface of my desk.

"Thanks for taking such good care of me," I said as I left the office.

"My pleasure, sir," said Walter.

I reached my car in the parking lot, when I realized I had forgotten my briefcase. I walked quickly back to my office. As I approached the door I heard a voice coming from inside. The handle to Walter's broom held my door slightly ajar. I pushed it open silently. On the wall above my computer were pictures of each of my children. Walter was cleaning the glass on each picture and talking to each child. "What a beautiful girl you are, Sharlene," he said as he wiped my daughter's picture clean. I must have made some noise at that point, because Walter turned around. His cheeks reddened when he saw me standing in the doorway.

"I just forgot my briefcase," I explained. I picked it up and started out the door. "Thanks again for taking such good care of my office." Walter saluted me with a roll of paper towels.

On the way home I mused about how Walter could have known Sharlene's name. The more I thought about it, the more intrigued I became. Walter had been a regular fixture around our office for several years. He was not very tall and was slightly stoop-shouldered. Although he had not yet turned forty, he was nearly bald. He had rather large, protruding ears and a nose that appeared as if he had taken a punch that left it flattened on his face. Much of the top of his head and his left cheek were blotched with a wine-colored birthmark. He was not a very attractive man. Yet I realized that I knew very little about him. He was a tireless worker as far as our office was concerned. We never had to worry about the wastebaskets being emptied. The carpeted floors were always vacuumed, and the tile floors gleamed brilliantly. Until tonight I had never noticed that not only were my windows always spotless, but so were the framed pictures and awards above my computer. I began to wonder about Walter.

The next day I asked my secretary what she knew about him. "Oh, he and his wife live about two blocks over," she said, pointing south of our building. "I've never met her, but he speaks very highly of his wife. He's told me how beautiful she is. That's kind of hard to believe—I mean, he's kind of hard to look at. But then, I guess it takes all kinds." She thought for a moment. "You know, I really don't know much about him, and he's worked here for about ten years. I think he's a pretty private person."

That is strange, I thought. My secretary was a walking book of knowledge on the people in our building. She always kept me aware of upcoming birthdays, weddings, funerals, and important events. "When's his birthday?" I asked her.

Her forehead wrinkled. "I can't remember. Let me check my file." She turned to her computer and punched a few keys. "That's funny," she said, "I don't have a birthday for him. I don't have much information at all. I probably haven't worried about him." She checked a few more files. "Want me to call personnel and get his birthday for you?"

I didn't want her to realize I was just testing her. "Sure," I said.

Later that afternoon she walked into my office. "Walter's a Fourth of July baby," she said. "I guess that's why we've never celebrated it. We always have a holiday on his birthday. This year we'll do something the day before or the day after, okay?"

"Sounds good to me," I said, not really wanting to admit that it didn't matter to me.

❤

I was working late that afternoon still trying to finish my presentation, when I heard the key in the lock again. Walter stuck his head around the door.

"Sorry," he said, "this is getting to be a habit. I'll drop by later."

"No, come on in, Walter. You won't bother me, and I'm ready to call it a day."

"If you're sure . . ."

"I'm sure."

Walter proceeded to empty my wastebasket.

"Last night," I said, "when I came back, I heard you talking to my daughter's picture. I've wondered how you knew her name."

Walter laughed a low, melodious laugh. "Oh, sir, I know all the children. That's Sharlene and Rebecca, Sherri and Kati," he said, pointing to the line of pictures of our girls. "And that's Stan and Brenda, Derick and Bonnie, Brett and David."

"You even know the names of their spouses," I said, amazed.

"Oh, yes." He looked up with concern written on his face. "That doesn't bother you, does it, sir?"

"No, no, Walter, I'm rather flattered that you'd take the time to learn each of their names."

He smiled. "I think I know the names of all the people in the photographs in this building. You just ask the secretaries; they'll tell you the names." He pointed to the picture of my wife. "Janice, for example, seems to be a lovely lady." He continued dusting.

"Do you and your wife have children, Walter?"

He sighed. "No, sir, my beautiful Margaret and I have never been blessed with children." He smiled sadly and continued cleaning my office. I left for the night.

A few days later I was giving my presentation at another site. I noticed the wastepaper basket was overflowing when I arrived early in the morning. "They need a Walter," I said to John, my co-presenter. "This place could use a good cleaning."

John shook his head. "He's a weird duck, though. I'm never very comfortable around him. Never says much, and that port-wine birthmark—I don't know, I'm just a little uncomfortable. But you sure can't fault his work. My office is always spotless."

"As is mine," I agreed.

Later that afternoon, as I returned to my office and began unloading the equipment I had used, Walter appeared. He had been weeding the flower beds outside our office.

"Can I help you, sir?"

"You bet. I never turn down a willing hand." Walter helped me unload the equipment and place it back on the shelves. I thanked him.

"No problem. Happy to be of service." He covered his head with a straw hat and returned to the flower beds.

♥

At our next staff meeting a new program was announced to honor employees who had done an extraordinary job. I raised my hand. "How about Walter? I've never seen anyone give as much to a job as he does. He might be a good choice."

There was some hemming and hawing around the table. "He may do a good job, but I can't imagine putting his picture out in the foyer. He'd frighten people away." There were some uncomfortable chuckles among the staff. "Anyone else have an idea?" A secretary from personnel was chosen.

I thought about Walter. Maybe they were right, I began to rationalize. Maybe putting his picture in the foyer would subject him to ridicule. The picture could be retouched, I thought, and the birthmark removed. But would Walter be offended? In the end I decided the rest of the staff were right; the secretary from personnel was a good choice. But it still gnawed on me.

That night, as my wife and I were walking, she could tell something was on my mind. I told her about the day's decision. "What is Walter like?" she asked.

I described him with his big ears, flat nose, and port-wine stain. I mentioned his bald head and his stooped shoulders.

"If that's what you see when you see Walter, you probably made the right decision," Janice said. We walked on in silence.

❤

Nearly two months passed. The picture of the secretary from personnel had been placed on an easel in the foyer. The following month it was replaced by the picture of a secretary from the finance department. After that fateful staff meeting, every time I saw Walter my gaze was focused on the deep red stain on his head and face.

One night I returned from a late afternoon presentation in Logan. It was dark as I pulled into the nearly vacant parking lot at our office. I began unloading equipment from my van, when I heard a familiar voice. "Can I be of service, sir?"

I smiled. "You're here late, Walter."

"Just heading home, sir," he said. "But I'd be pleased to help you get your equipment tucked away." Within ten minutes we had put everything on the shelves.

"Are you walking, Walter?"

"I only live a few blocks away."

"Let me give you a ride. You're on my way."

"I'd be pleased," he said, "if you're sure it's not out of your way."

He directed me to his house. The yard was as neat and clean as I expected it to be. I pulled into his driveway.

"You look tired, sir," he said to me. "Would you like to come in and have something to drink?"

My first inclination was to thank him and go, but my

curiosity was too strong. "That would be wonderful, Walter," I said. He grinned as he opened the door of my van.

"You'll get to meet my beautiful bride, Margaret," he said as we headed for the front door. The front-porch light was burning brightly, but there were no lights on in the house. "Margaret always turns it on to welcome me home," he said, pointing to the light. He opened the front door and switched on the living room light. "Come in, come in," he said.

The living room of Walter's home was immaculate. He motioned me toward the couch. "I'll be just a minute," he said. "Margaret, my love, we have company," he called out. A light came on in the kitchen. I heard the refrigerator door open and close, followed by the sound of ice cubes being dropped in a glass. A moment later Walter reentered the living room with a glass of juice in his right hand and a beautiful woman with her hand on his left arm. I stood up to greet her.

"Margaret, let me introduce you to my good friend, Mr. Siddoway. He's the one with the eight lovely children."

Margaret extended her hand toward me and I took it in mine. She walked to a chair near the front door and sat down. "Walter tells me how wonderful your children are," she said.

"Well, I'm prejudiced, but I've nothing to complain about," I replied.

"I hope your daughters all turn out to be beautiful and kind and your sons as handsome and gentle as my Walter." I held the glass to my lips and tried not to show my reaction.

"Now, Margaret," he said, clearly embarrassed. "I hope his daughters turn out as beautiful as you." There was a spirit of love and warmth within their living room.

She giggled. "Oh, Walter, you always know what to say."

I finished my drink. "I'd better be going. My wife will wonder where I am." Walter took the glass from me. "It's been a pleasure to meet you, Margaret," I said. "Walter speaks so highly of you."

"Ah, my handsome Walter. Always the gentleman. Always willing to give service. Just like the Master."

I extended my hand toward Margaret. She didn't respond. "Sweetheart," said Walter quietly, "Mr. Siddoway is standing in front of you and slightly to your left. He'd like to shake your hand."

"I'm sorry," she said, reaching out in my general direction. I took her hand.

"Margaret's been blind since birth," said Walter.

Not as blind as I, I thought on the way home.